CONCORDIA UNIVERSITY

SB123.B82   C001 V008
HOW PLANTS ARE TRAINED TO WORK FOR

3 4211 000097306

WITHDRAWN

DATE DUE

MR1 3 '96			

D1226585

DEMCO 38-297

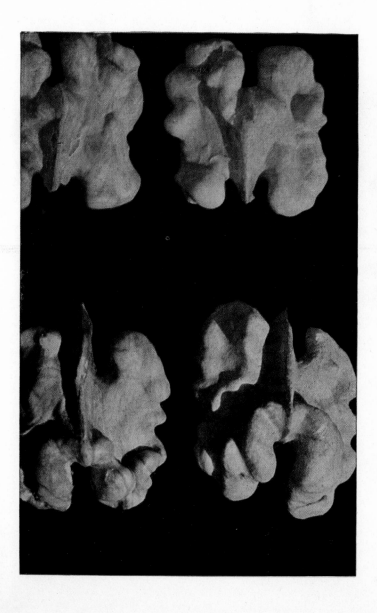

SANTA ROSA NUT MEATS

In developing the Santa Rosa walnut, Mr. Burbank had in mind not merely thinness of shell and abundant bearing, but also the various qualities of meat that are desirable. Among other things, he eliminated the superfluous tannin, which gives the nut a disagreeable astringency as well as brownish color. The whiteness of the meats of the Santa Rosa is evidence of his success in this regard.

SANTA ROSA NUT MEATS

In developing the Santa Rosa walnut, Mr. Burbank had in mind not merely thinness of shell and abundant bearing, but also the various qualities of meat that are desirable. Among other things, he eliminated the superfluous tannin, which gives the nut a disagreeable astringency as well as brownish color. The whiteness of the meats of the Santa Rosa is evidence of his success in this regard.

HOW PLANTS ARE TRAINED
TO WORK FOR MAN
BY LUTHER BURBANK Sc. D

TREES · BIOGRAPHY · INDEX

VOLUME VIII

247   84

EIGHT VOLUMES · ILLUSTRATED
PREFATORY NOTE BY DAVID STARR JORDAN

P. F. COLLIER & SON COMPANY
NEW YORK

KLINCK MEMORIAL LIBRARY
Concordia Teachers College
River Forest. Illinois

Copyright, 1914
BY THE LUTHER BURBANK SOCIETY
All rights reserved

Copyright, 1914
BY THE LUTHER BURBANK SOCIETY
Entered at Stationers' Hall, London
All rights reserved

Copyright, 1915
BY THE LUTHER BURBANK SOCIETY
Entered at Stationers' Hall, London
All rights reserved

Copyright, 1921
BY P. F. COLLIER & SON COMPANY

MANUFACTURED IN U. S. A.

64802

CONTENTS

	PAGE
NUTS AS A PROFITABLE CROP . . .	7
THE PAPER SHELL AND OTHER WALNUTS	27
THE CHESTNUT—BEARING NUTS AT SIX MONTHS	51
THE HICKORY NUT — AND OTHER NUTS	77
GROWING TREES FOR LUMBER . . .	97
TREES WHOSE PRODUCTS ARE USEFUL SUBSTANCES	125
TREES AND SHRUBS FOR SHADE AND ORNAMENT	149
PERSONAL AND HISTORICAL	175
THE STORY OF LUTHER BURBANK . .	217
MY EARLY YEARS AT SANTA ROSA .	243
PATIENCE AND ITS REWARD	271
A SUMMARY OF THE WORK . . .	309
THE BEARING OF THIS WORK ON HUMAN LIFE	349

LIST OF ILLUSTRATIONS

SANTA ROSA NUT MEATS . *Frontispiece*

PAGE

A DWARF CHESTNUT TREE 10

A BASKET OF CHESTNUTS 16

THE PAPER SHELL ON THE TREE . . 30

SANTA ROSA WALNUTS 36

PARENTS AND OFFSPRING 44

SIX-MONTHS-OLD CHESTNUT TREE IN
BEARING 54

YEARLING CHESTNUT TREE IN BEARING 58

A SIX-MONTHS-OLD CHESTNUT TREE . 62

BUR AND CATKIN 66

WELL PROTECTED 70

CHESTNUTS IN THE BUR 74

HICKORY NUTS 80

A PECAN TREE 84

A VARIETY OF TROPICAL NUTS . . . 88

CHINQUAPINS AND CHESTNUTS . . . 92

PAGE

THE WILD NUTMEG 104

OLIVE TREES 116

THE CALIFORNIA CHINQUAPIN AS AN
    ORNAMENTAL TREE 130

THE VARIEGATED BOX ELDER . . . 138

AN ACACIA TREE IN BLOOM . . . 144

A YOUNG SEQUOIA GIGANTEA . . . 152

THE LARGEST TREE IN THE WORLD . 158

YELLOW PINE 162

THE JUDAS TREE OR RED-BUD . . . 166

THE HYBRID ELM 170

OLIVE ROSS BURBANK, LUTHER BUR-
    BANK'S MOTHER 184

LUTHER BURBANK'S BIRTHPLACE . . 202

THE OLD HOMESTEAD AS IT NOW APPEARS 212

MRS. LUTHER BURBANK 224

LUTHER BURBANK AT THE AGE OF
    TWENTY-FIVE 246

MY FIRST ADVERTISEMENT 252

VIEW IN THE SANTA ROSA GARDENS . 258

MIDSUMMER'S VIEW 266

PAGE

A SIMPLE BUT IMPORTANT EQUIPMENT 274

SOIL-STIRRING IMPLEMENTS 280

SEEDS IN THE GREENHOUSE 286

CLEANING SEEDS 292

A COLLECTION OF SIEVES 298

MARKING ROWS FOR PLANTING . . . 304

PERMANENT LABELS 312

AN EFFECTIVE IMPLEMENT 318

HYBRIDS AND PARENTS 324

UNNAMED BEAUTIES 330

TIGRIDIA SEEDS AT WHOLESALE . . . 336

MIDSUMMER AT SANTA ROSA . . . 342

BACK VIEW OF MY HOME SHOWING
    VINES 354

TROPICAL LUXURIANCE 362

A STRIKING CONTRAST IN SEEDLINGS . 370

NUTS AS A PROFITABLE CROP

THE BUSINESS SIDE OF NUT GROWING

"A CHESTNUT *bush!*" exclaimed a visitor; "that is the greatest marvel I have seen yet. I was brought up under chestnut *trees;* but when I see chestnuts growing on huckleberry bushes I am certainly having a new experience."

And no doubt this experience would be new to almost anyone who has not visited my experiment farm at Sebastopol. For, so far as known to me until very recently, there have been no chestnuts growing on bushes anywhere else in the world. But there are plenty of them in the orchard at Sebastopol; that is to say, if a sprig of a shrub only three feet or so in height and three feet across is entitled to be called a bush.

Moreover the nuts that are borne on these miniature trees are of the finest variety—large, plump nuts, at least as large as half a dozen of the ordinary eastern nuts you are likely to find

7

growing on chestnut trees of the largest size;
and they are sweet in flavor.

If it is added that some varieties of the new
chestnuts bear when only six months old, when
grown from seed—rivaling corn or wheat, and
seeming quite to forget the traditions of their
own tribe—a further glimpse will be given of
the modification that scientific plant development has wrought in the status of the nut-
bearing tree.

No other tree, to be sure, quite rivals the chestnut in this regard; but some of the new walnuts
bear at eighteen months of age, which is quite
remarkable enough. And in general the time of
bearing of these nuts has been so hastened that
the growing of a walnut orchard to-day is an
altogether different matter from what it was
a generation ago.

Moreover, a way has been found to induce the
walnut tree to grow about four times as fast as
it formerly did; and the wood of the tree is of
the finest quality for the use of cabinetmakers.
Of course the latter fact is of incidental interest
only to the grower of nuts; yet it is not quite a
negligible factor. And, from another standpoint, obviously, the wood-producing capacities
of the new trees have a high degree of
importance.

These and a few other transformations in the nut-bearing trees, brought about by careful selective breeding, have prepared the way for an entire change of attitude of the horticulturist toward the question of producing nuts as a business, comparable to the business of the fruit grower.

THE FOOD VALUE OF NUTS

Meantime there has been a marked change of attitude on the part of the medical profession, and, following them, of the general public, as to the value of nuts in the dietary.

In fact, nuts have most substantial merits as food, and these merits are yearly coming to be more fully recognized. In the older countries, nuts have already assumed—indeed have long held—a position of economic importance, and convincing evidence of their growing recognition in America is found in the reports of experiment stations of the Agricultural Bureau, which in recent years have from time to time urged the merits of various nuts upon the attention of growers. A study of the market reports shows that nuts of many kinds are handled on a commercial scale in our cities.

There should be nothing surprising in this; for, of course, in a wide view nuts are the seeds of fruits, and there is no obvious reason why they

A DWARF CHESTNUT TREE

*This bushlike tree is an example of
our hybrid chestnuts. The workman
who stands beside the tree is five feet
seven inches tall. Note the abundant
crop of nuts on the tree and under the
tree. Gathering chestnuts becomes a
simple matter when the trees are of
this type. This tree bore its first crop
of nuts eight months after the seed
was planted, and has now borne ten full
crops of nuts when only ten years
of age.*

should not have unusual dietetic value. More-over they are for the most part grown on peren-nial shrubs or trees rather than on succulent and perishable annuals, and thus have close relation-ship with the fruits of the orchard.

But the fact that nut-bearing trees for the most part have received no special attention from the cultivator of the soil, their product being gathered only casually, has caused them to be regarded as wild products not falling within the scope of the horticulturist. In most parts of the United States the nut-bearing trees have received no attention whatever from the cultivator of the soil, and their product has been regarded as a more or less superfluous luxury, rather than as having dietetic consequence.

In the Gulf States and in California, in recent years, there has been a radical change of attitude. In these regions the cultivation of nuts is already becoming an industry of great importance More recently, the industry has extended to New York and even to Canada. Meantime, the use of nuts on the table in all parts of the United States has become more and more habitual, and they are beginning to take their proper place among the important products of the soil. Their recognition as really valuable foods is so com-paratively recent, however, that it would not be superfluous to briefly run over the list of commercial nuts, with reference to their food values and their present and prospective economic importance.

Such an outline may advantageously prepare the way for the detailed account of the experimental work through which new varieties of several of the more important nuts have been developed.

The Chief Marketable Nuts

The marketable nuts include almonds, Brazil nuts, filberts, hickory nuts, pecans, Persian or English walnuts, chestnuts, butternuts, walnuts pine nuts, peanuts, and coconuts, not to mention several less known and little used species.

The coconut, the fruit of a palm tree, is indigenous to tropical and subtropical regions, and may very likely have played a part in the history of developing man not unlike that ascribed to the date and the fig. It is still a most important article of diet to inhabitants of tropical islands, being prized not merely for the meat of the nut but for the milky fluid which it furnishes in large quantity. The natives sacrifice the partially ripe nut for the sake of the milk, but most northerners find this a taste to be acquired with some effort.

The meat of the ripe nut, as it comes to the northern market, is extremely palatable, and in a dried state, grated, it is widely employed to flavor sundry delicacies.

The coconut is raised extensively in Cuba, and to a limited extent in Florida and lower California, the total number of these nuts produced in the United States in 1899 being 145,000.

Most of the other nuts are similarly used as accessories of diet, for variety rather than as substantials. They are capable, however, of playing a more important rôle, as the chemical analysis of their constituents shows that they are in the main highly concentrated foods, having little waste aside from the shells. They contain all the important constituents of diet—proteins, fats, and carbohydrates—and are thus in themselves capable of sustaining life. They do not contain the various elements in proper proportion, however, to make them suitable for an exclusive diet. Moreover, their highly concentrated character makes them somewhat difficult of digestion if taken in too large quantities.

The chestnut differs from the other nuts in having a relatively high percentage of starchy matter, 42 per cent of its edible portion being found in the carbohydrate division—a proportion which no other nut except the acorn

approaches. The amount of fat in the chestnut is proportionately small—only about 5½
per cent, as against the 64.4 per cent of the
English walnut and the 71.2 per cent of the
pecan.

As to protein—muscle-forming matter—the
chestnut has but a little over 6 per cent, while the
English walnut has 16.7 per cent, and the
American black walnut and the butternut head
the list with 27.6 per cent and 27.9 per cent
respectively.

Chestnuts when fresh have a very much higher
percentage of water than other nuts—no less
than 45 per cent, whereas nuts in general have
but three to five per cent.

It appears, then, that the meat of the chestnut
furnishes a less concentrated food than other
nuts supply, but one that is rich in digestible
starches, of which it contains six or seven times
the proportion common to other nuts. This
excess of starchy constituents explains why the
chestnut is not generally relished so much as
many other nuts in the raw state. But it explains
also why this nut may be eaten in quantity when
cooked.

In France and Italy chestnuts are very generally eaten, usually being prepared by boiling,
and they constitute a really significant item in

the dietary of the poorer classes. Large quantities of the nuts are also dried and ground to a flour, which keeps for some time without deteriorating, and from which sweet and nutritious cakes are made. It is said that in Korea the chestnut takes a place in the dietary not unlike that which the potato occupies with us, being used raw, boiled, roasted, or cooked with meat.

PRODUCTION AND VALUE OF NUTS

Until the chestnut blight came in very recent years, threatening the entire growth of chestnut trees in the northeastern United States, there seemed a good prospect that the cultivation of this nut would become an important industry in the near future.

Meantime, there is no present indication that the other nuts indigenous to the northern parts of the United States are likely to be extensively cultivated until they have profited by the experiments of the plant developer. The thick shells of hickory nuts and butternuts, and of the native walnuts, interfere with their commercial value. We shall consider in another connection the possibility of remedying these defects, but for the moment the nuts that are grown on a commercial scale are almost solely those that will flourish in the warmer climates, and hence the industries

A BASKET OF CHESTNUTS

These are chestnuts of mixed heritage, combining the traits of European, American, and Japanese species. Their large size seems all the more remarkable when it is known that they are grown on pygmy bushes, quite unlike the chestnut trees with which most of us are familiar.

associated with their production are confined mostly to the Gulf States and to the Pacific Coast.

To be sure, the aggregate wild nut crop of the Central and Northern States represents a considerable value. But no official estimate has been made as to the precise figures involved. In general, the nuts obtained from such trees are not looked upon as a commercial crop. They are for the most part consumed on the farm or in neighboring villages.

Only three kinds of nuts are grown on a commercial scale in the United States at the present time, these being the Persian or English walnut, the pecan, and the almond.

According to the official reports of the Census Bureau, the total nut crop reported for 1909 was 62,328,000 pounds. This was 55.7 per cent greater than the crop reported for 1899, and the value, $4,448,000, was 128.1 per cent greater. "California is by far the most important State in the production of nuts, and Texas ranks next. No other State reported as much as $100,000 worth of nuts in 1909."

The Census Report takes note of nuts other than the three just named, but the total value of all the others is relatively insignificant, the combined value of the Persian walnuts, pecans, and almonds amounting to $3,981,000, or about nine-tenths of the total for all nuts.

Perhaps the most interesting feature of the report on the production of nuts is the very rapid increase in recent years. The crop of Persian or English walnuts in 1909, for example, was more than twice as great as that ten years earlier. The production of pecans in 1909 was more than three times as great as in 1899. The production of almonds, on the other hand, had decreased somewhat in the decade under consideration.

As to the actual number of trees under cultivation, the almond heads the list, the trees in bearing in 1910 numbering 1,187,962, and young trees not in bearing numbering 389,575. By far the greater number of these are in California, which has 1,166,730 almond trees in bearing, whereas Arizona, the second State, has only 6,639, and all other States combined have only 14,593. The total production of almonds in 1909 was 6,793,539 pounds, with a value of $711,970.

The almond is a native of western Asia, and has been cultivated from time immemorial. It is mentioned in the Scriptures as one of the chief products of the land of Canaan. In California it has been more or less under cultivation since about 1853. The best manner of its cultivation, however, was not well understood, and the greater ease and certainty with which the walnut can be grown has led to the abandonment in recent years of many of the almond orchards.

Nevertheless, the crop is one of considerable importance, as the figures just given show.

The total number of Persian or English walnut trees in bearing in 1910 numbered 914,270, of which all but about sixty thousand are in California. The rapid increase of the industry, and its prospect of still greater increase in the near future, is shown in the fact that the number of young trees, not yet of bearing age, was reported in 1910 as 806,413.

The extension of the industry is shown also in the fact that of the trees not yet in bearing no fewer than 177,004 are in the single State of Oregon, and 5,513 in Mississippi. These figures forecast the spread of industry to meet the growing demand for walnuts in America.

The total production of Persian walnuts in 1909 was 22,026,524 pounds, with a valuation of $2,297,336.

It will thus be seen that the walnut takes rank as a commercial crop of genuine importance. The value of the crop approaches that of the total crop of apricots, although not as yet approaching the value of the half dozen more popular orchard fruits.

THE CULTIVATION OF THE PECAN

In 1899 the pecan ranked third among nut-producing trees, both as regards number of trees under cultivation and actual product. The pecan trees in bearing at that time numbered 643,292, with a net product of 3,206,850 pounds.

In the ten succeeding years the pecan industry came ahead very rapidly, and in 1910 the pecan was second to the almond as to number of trees in bearing, and second to the Persian walnut as to weight and value of its crop. Moreover, the number of pecan trees under cultivation, but not yet of bearing age in 1910, was actually larger than the number of trees in bearing; showing a surprisingly rapid increase of the industry.

The actual number of pecan trees in bearing in 1910 was 1,619,521, and the number of young trees under cultivation 1,685,066, making a total of 3,304,587, a number in excess of the combined numbers of almond and Persian walnut trees under cultivation.

The production of pecans in 1909 was 9,890,769 pounds, with a value of $971,596. The total production of 1899 was only 3,206,850 pounds. Thus, as already noted, the production increased by more than three hundred per cent in ten years. There seems every prospect that the increase will be still more rapid in the coming decade.

Peculiar interest attaches to the pecan because it is the one nut indigenous to the United States among those that at present have actual commercial importance. The pecan, indeed, must be looked to as now holding the position in the southern portions of the United States that the chestnut should occupy in the northern—that of premier nut. In recent years its merits have begun to receive wide attention, as the figures just quoted show, and the cultivation of pecan nuts for the market is likely to become a very important industry. Already there are numerous named varieties on the market, each having its champions.

These varieties have peculiar interest because of the fact that each one of them represents not an artificially developed product, as in the case of most varieties of fruits and grains, but merely the progeny of an individual tree.

It appears that here and there, particularly in the State of Mississippi, there has grown a pecan tree of unknown antecedents that became locally famous for the large size and unusual quality of its fruit.

These trees, it will be understood, are all of one species, and the nuts are obviously all of one

kind; no one would think of mistaking any one
of them for anything but a pecan. Yet the
individuality—the personality—of each tree is
revealed in the average character as to size,
shape, and peculiarities of shell and kernel, of its
fruit, and also as to the great difference in productiveness and earliness or lateness of bearing.

THE VARIETIES OF PECAN NUTS

Of course such individuality is precisely what
we have become accustomed to expect in orchard
fruits and other plants under cultivation. But
until recently it has not been generally understood that such diversity is commonly to be
found among wild plants. So the case of the
pecan furnishes an interesting illustration of the
variation of plants in the wild state. The pecan
trees that show these individual variations are
precisely like the cultivated varieties of orchard
fruits in that they do not breed true from seed.
Doubtless it might be possible to develop true
fixed varieties from each of them by selective
breeding, but this is not necessary any more than
in the case of orchard fruits. For, like other
trees, the pecan may be propagated by grafting
or budding.

Nothing more is necessary than to make cuttings of twigs or buds from the parent stock,

grafting these as cions on an ordinary pecan stock, to produce new trees in indefinite numbers, all of which retain the precise quality of the parent.

Such grafts were made in the case of each of a score or so of the famous individual pecans above referred to, with the result that as many varieties have been given assured permanency. For the most part, these varieties have been named after the location where the parent tree grew, as the San Saba, the Rome; or else after the original owner or an early cultivator, as the Jewett, the Pabst, the Post, the Russell, the Stuart.

According to a recent report of the Department of Agriculture, there are ten of these varieties that have now been advertised and propagated for a sufficient time to gain wide distribution.

Extensive orchards of pecans are now under cultivation in almost all of the Southern States; yet the industry is so recent that, with a single exception, the parent trees of all the ten prominent varieties are still alive and in a more or less vigorous condition of bearing.

Unfortunately the pecan is restricted as to habitat, but it flourishes as far north as St. Louis in the Mississippi Valley, in all the Gulf States;

including Texas, and along the south Atlantic
seaboard. Texas is the chief producer (5,832,367
pounds in 1909), Oklahoma second (894,172
pounds), and Louisiana third (723,578 pounds).
Without doubt hardier varieties, which may be
grown farther north, may in time be developed.

Meantime it is held with reason that within the
territory to which it is naturally adapted, no
other nut, native or foreign, can be considered to
compete with it.

The qualities of the pecan as a dessert and
confectioners' nut are familiar to everyone; but
the best varieties have hitherto been raised in
restricted quantities, and hence have not found
their way extensively into the northern markets.
With the increase of the industry to commercial
proportions, this defect will soon be remedied,
and the pecan may be expected to advance rapidly in popular favor. But, for that matter, the
demand already greatly exceeds the supply.

Observation of the deferred recognition of the
merits of the pecan suggests the inquiry as to
whether there may not be other indigenous nuts
that have similarly been ignored.

There is certainly not another of comparable
merit, but there is at least one neglected one that
the amateur at any rate might find worthy of
attention, whatever its defects from a commer-

cial standpoint. This is the familiar hazelnut, a near relative of the European filbert. The hazelnut is smaller than its European cousin, but it is of course susceptible of improvement in that regard; and the hardy nature of the shrub makes it suitable for waste lands, or as an adjunct to the chestnut orchard, even far to the north, but none of this class are suited to dry, warm climates.

The hickory, the black walnut, and the butternut, already referred to as of doubtful commercial value, are nuts that may well appeal more confidently to the amateur. They grow wild in many regions of the Middle West where the chestnut is not indigenous, and the black walnut and hickory in particular are widely famed for their lumber—or were before the vandalism of the early settlers practically exhausted the supply. As to palatability, there are many persons who would be disposed to place the butternut near the head of the list of edible nuts; and no one will deny the fine quality of hickories and some of the black walnuts.

All in all, the opportunity for diversion and profit in this unexplored direction seems peculiarly inviting; and it is one that is likely to be eagerly seized by an increasing number of growers as the years go by. The fact that nut-bearing

trees add permanent beauty to the landscape
gives them an additional claim on the interest of
that growing body of city dwellers who are nowadays harking back to the soil for esthetic rather
than for commercial reasons. Meantime the further fact that an unfruitful tree may ultimately
be valuable as lumber should make additional
appeal to those nature lovers who, though calling
themselves amateurs, enjoy none the less to have
their hobbies bring them a certain monetary
return.

THE PAPER SHELL AND OTHER WALNUTS

The Method Used to Produce Them

THE fact that more than 13,000 tons of walnuts are now raised annually in California, chiefly for shipment to the eastern markets as against 2,300 tons raised in the year 1895, suggests better than any amount of commentary, the growth of this new industry.

Part, at least, of the increased popularity of the walnut may be ascribed to the introduction of varieties having thin shells and more delicious meats. All Persian, or so-called English, walnuts have relatively thin shells as compared with the American walnuts, but the production of the "paper-shell" varieties puts these nuts in a class quite by themselves.

And this matter of the shell is one of real significance from the standpoint of the consumer. A nut like the American walnut, which can be cracked with difficulty, requiring the use of a hammer, can never gain great popularity. The difficulties encountered in extracting the meat of the nut are too great. But a nut that has a shell so thin that it can easily be crushed in the fingers is sure to make its way and to be found more and more generally on the dinner table.

The terms "paper-shell" and "soft-shell" as applied to the walnut are interchangeable. There are now several varieties of walnuts on the market that are generally classified under one head or the other. Their name merely refers to the ease with which the nut can be cracked. As to this there is great variation among ordinary walnuts, and the soft-shell varieties also show a diversity. But the best varieties are so friable that they can readily be crushed in the fingers.

The walnut is so variable that it is possible for the plant developer to consult his own wishes in the matter of modifying its shell. I have developed a variety in which the shell became so soft that it could readily be penetrated by birds; in fact, also, a nut that had a mere rim of shell, being thus comparable to the stoneless plum. There would be no difficulty in maintaining this variety of shell-less walnuts, but its thinness of shell was a disadvantage, and I found it desirable to breed the variety back to a somewhat thicker shell covering, by striking a compromise

64802

between the old hard-shell varieties and a nut that was practically without its protecting shell.

One of the thin-shelled new walnuts was introduced under the name of the Santa Rosa Soft Shell. It was produced by the usual method of selective breeding, and in producing it, of course, other qualities were in mind besides the thinness of shell. In particular, selection was made for early and abundant bearing, whiteness and palatability of meat, with absence of tannin—it being tannin which gives the brown color and bitter taste to the older or ordinary walnuts. The perfected Santa Rosa may be depended upon to give much larger crops than the French variety known as the Franquette.

It should be explained, however, that there are two varieties of the Santa Rosa. One blooms with the ordinary walnut trees, while the other, like the Franquette, blooms two weeks later, generally escaping the frost that sometimes affect the early bloomer. In producing the new soft shell, nuts of the ordinary walnut were tested from many sources. There is great variation among these nuts, and some were found that were almost entirely without shells. One seedling had nuts with the meats half exposed; that is, with shell covering a portion of its surface, suggesting the abortive stone of the little

THE PAPER SHELL ON
THE TREE

In the course of experiments we have produced walnuts that were devoid of shell, but this proved a disadvantage as the birds soon learned the secret. It was necessary, therefore, to select specimens with thin shells, instead of those with no shells, to continue the experiment. The ones here shown have shells of the ideal thickness and delicious white meats.

French plum from which the race of stoneless plums was developed.

By selection among the seedlings of this almost shell-less walnut, it was found that a walnut without any shell, bearing simply a husk, could readily be produced. But, as just related, the birds were quickly aware of the fact, and soon taught me that, except for its scientific interest, the shell-less walnut had no value.

After that the experiment in walnut breeding was carried on in a somewhat different direction, a shell being obviously desirable. In due time two varieties were developed that had the shell of just the right consistency; combining this trait with the habit of early and abundant bearing and excellent quality of the nuts themselves.

Cions from these trees, grafted and regrafted, make up the race of true Santa Rosa Soft Shells. I am informed, however, that trees grown from the seed have been extensively sold as Santa Rosas, although they may depart very widely from the characteristics of the parent form.

The name cannot be applied with propriety to any trees except those that are grown by grafting, for the walnut is a variable tree and cannot be depended upon to come true from the seed.

The original Santa Rosa, however, was grown from seed, and of course, it was necessary in perfecting the varieties to grow successive generations in the same way.

The parent tree was a walnut growing in San Francisco. It bore the most valuable nuts of the kind that had ever been seen in California. Mr. Alfred Wright first called my attention to this tree about thirty years ago. I found that it bore not only abundantly but regularly, and that the nuts were of exceedingly fine quality, and of relatively thin shell, their chief fault being that the two halves would sometimes separate slightly, leaving the meat exposed to the air, so that the meat did not keep as well as if in a thoroughly sealed shell.

The original tree was destroyed soon after my attention was called to it, to make room for a street, but I had secured nuts and had a colony of seedlings under inspection. Among these there was a great variation, giving me good opportunity for selection. Selection being made with reference to all the desirable qualities of the walnut in addition to thinness of shell, presently there was developed a variety that seemed worthy of introduction, and cions and trees from this were sent out under the name of Santa Rosa.

The nuts of this variety are of medium size, ripening about three weeks earlier than any other walnuts then grown in the State. The meat is white and unsurpassed in flavor. The thin shell is also light-colored. The tree bears enormous crops, and about its only defect is that it may, on occasion, be caught by the late spring frosts. But even with this defect, it produces a larger crop of nuts than any other tree that I have seen.

Without doubt the most productive walnut tree in America and perhaps on earth is one of these Santa Rosas, now standing at Campbell, Santa Clara County, California. The owner writes me as follows: "Regarding the Santa Rosa walnut tree, we kept no record of the first few crops. The record since is as follows:

1897	. . . .	250 lbs.	1904	. . .	. 481 lbs.
1898	. . . .	300 "	1905	. . . .	250 "
1899	. . . .	229 "	1906	. . . .	200 "
1900	. . . .	600 "	1907	. . . .	380 "
1901	. . . .	237 "	1908	. . . .	712 "
1902	. . . .	478 "	1909	. . . .	575 "
1903	. . . .	380 "	1910	. . . .	600 "

These nuts have always sold for from two to five cents more per pound than the 'No. 1's' from southern California."

Combining with the Japanese Walnut

The Paradox has extraordinary qualities of growth, but it is almost sterile, producing only a few nuts on an entire tree, and these nuts of the poorest quality.

Another hybridizing experiment that had great interest was that in which the Persian walnut was crossed with the Japanese walnut, known as *Juglans Sieboldii*. The Persian walnut in these crosses was used as the pistillate parent.

The first generation hybrids of this cross show a combination of qualities of the two parent species as regards the nuts, which are not borne abundantly. The foliage is very much larger, however, than that of either species, the bark is white, and the tree itself is of enormously enhanced growth. It probably makes about twice as much wood in a given period as either of the parent species. The leaves are quite hairy on both sides, even more so than those of the Japanese parent. The branches are inclined to droop.

The nuts of the Japanese walnut have an exceedingly hard shell. The meat of the nut, however, is delicious, perhaps equaling that of any other nut, with the exception of some varieties of the pecan. But it is very difficult to get the

When Burbank Was Just
a Beginner

THE picturesque New England town of Lancaster,
Massachusetts, was a rendezvous for ministers, lecturers, and teachers, and was charged to an unusual degree
with intellectual activity. Into this environment, March 7,
1849, was born Luther Burbank, the thirteenth child of
Olive Ross and Samuel Walton Burbank.

Luther was a quiet, serious child, whose most noticeable
trait was a love for flowers that amounted almost to reverence. From his earliest boyhood he studied plants, trees,
fruits, garden vegetables—in fact, everything that grew
from the earth.

But plants did not demand his entire attention. He received an excellent fundamental education at Lancaster
Academy, took great interest in chemistry and mechanics,
learned the useful trade of carpentry, and for a time
worked in a factory near his home. At twenty years of
age, Burbank decided that a physician's profession would
be most congenial as a life work, and began the study of
medicine. However, the death of his father caused him to
abandon this purpose.

Soon after Samuel Burbank's death the family moved to
Groton—now known as Ayer, Massachusetts; and Luther
purchased a seventeen-acre farm in the nearby village of
Lunenburg, to be used for raising seeds and garden products. This was the beginning of definite experiments with
plants.

The Burbank potato, Burbank's most famous product,
also his first, was evolved largely by accident in his early
experiments on the Lunenburg farm. A rare seed-ball of
the Early Rose potato afforded the material which made
possible this valuable discovery. Burbank planted the
twenty-three tiny seeds the ball contained and selected one
of the resulting plants as possessing the best qualities.

In 1875, after three years at Lunenburg, Burbank suddenly decided to move to California.

Ten Burbank potatoes, retained by their originator and
constituting Burbank's most tangible asset in beginning his

new career in California, were planted on his brother's farm, and the entire product of the first season was saved and replanted; so that by the end of the second season the stock was large enough to offer for sale.

But victory was not won without an heroic struggle and years of persistent effort, for it should be remembered that Burbank was blazing a new path—a path that others may now follow with comparative ease, since he has cleared the way.

During the fourth year at Santa Rosa an incident of momentous importance occurred, an event that proved to be the definite turning point toward marked success. Burbank received a "rush" order from Mr. Warren Dutton, a wealthy merchant and banker of Tomales, who had become suddenly interested in prune growing and wished to undertake it on a large scale with the least possible delay. Mr. Dutton required 20,000 prune trees to be produced in a single season.

Though this was an unprecedented task, Burbank brought his ingenuity and resourcefulness to bear on the problem, and solved it to the consternation of a skeptical world. By placing French prune buds on the required number of almond seedlings, which sprout almost as readily as corn, the miracle was accomplished, and within the time specified. Never before or since, so far as is known, was a two-hundred-acre orchard developed in a single season.

At this point Burbank ceased to be just a beginner and entered the ranks of the successful plant breeders. The prune experiment served to advertise his work locally, and by cumulative degrees his fame spread throughout the nation and eventually became worldwide. By the end of the tenth year in California, the quality of the products and reliability of the Burbank "Santa Rosa Nursery" became so widely known that he was selling over $16,000 worth of trees and plants per year.

As the World Knows Burbank To-day

THE pioneer in any new line of thought is usually first ridiculed and frowned upon; then abused; later endured and pitied; and afterward accepted as an oracle. Such was the lot of Luther Burbank, but with patience and fortitude, not heeding the skeptics and cynics, he struggled forward from the humble position of lowliest beginner to the envied heights of the world's foremost plant breeder.

Burbank and Edison

Luther Burbank holds much the same place in the hearts and admiration of his fellow men as Thomas Edison. They have a great deal in common. Both are known as "wizards" and "geniuses," whereas their accomplishments have been chiefly the reward of hard work with intelligence to guide them; both have passed the traditional three score and ten years and are still tremendously keen in their enjoyment of life and work.

Thousands of people make pilgrimages to Burbank's experimental farm at Santa Rosa, in the hope that they may be permitted to see and talk with the famous "Plant Wizard." Visitors were welcomed until Burbank found it impossible to carry on his work and still meet personally the rapidly increasing number, many of whom had journeyed far to confer with him and to learn his methods. Among these were men and women prominent in literature, art, science, education, finance, those connected with governments of most foreign lands, and many whose names are familiar in song and story.

During the last ten years he has spared the time to see but few of those desiring an interview. Invitations to write and to lecture in this and other lands have necessarily been declined by him. He is too busy making plant history to devote his valuable time to public appearances or to playing host to visiting admirers.

A Glimpse of a Unique Genius

Although the name of Luther Burbank is familiar throughout the whole civilized world, and even where civili-

17

zation is but partial, yet very few appreciate fully how strenuous and comprehensive has been his work.

By practice and concentration, Burbank has developed his mental and physical powers to a most unusual degree. After fifty years of grueling and continuous effort, he is now able to conduct simultaneously and keep fully familiar with every detail of thousands of different experiments.

The responsiveness of the senses to conscious training is dramatically demonstrated by the following true incident which occurred at Santa Rosa. Some years ago Mr. Burbank passed a bed of verbenas just coming to blossom. Suddenly he stopped, dropped to his hands and knees and began crawling through the verbena bed. He had noticed the familiar trace of the delicate trailing arbutus odor coming from unscented verbenas. He searched until he had located the plant sending it forth, and then was ready to begin the production of a sweet-scented verbena. Yet Burbank says: "There is no magic in it; every person equipped with a good nose and a good pair of eyes can reach the same sensitiveness."

As a demonstration of his invincible patience when striving for a desired improvement, his work with the daisy may be taken as typical. In developing the Shasta Daisy, Burbank produced millions of plants and blossoms, destroyed ninety out of every hundred, and continued with the seeds of the survivors until he had developed the exact product he had visualized.

The great plant breeder spares neither time nor effort when working out his theories. He has recently completed an experiment, the result of which attracted nation-wide attention. Eighteen years ago he began, and has lately completed, the arduous task of retracing the evolution of corn from the Indian grass teosinte. By nature's un-aided and undirected processes it had taken generations to accomplish the evolution.

No Magic Wand

Like Antæus, Luther Burbank lives close to the soil and receives new strength from daily contact with it. He carries no wizard's wand, possesses no magic power. What he meats from the shell, as they are usually broken in cracking the nut.

There is, however, a form of the Japanese walnut which is so variant that it is sometimes regarded as a distinct species, under the name of *Juglans cordiformis,* but which I think not correctly entitled to this rank, inasmuch as the two forms are closely similar as to general appearance and growth. The chief difference is in the nuts, which in the *cordiformis* are usually heart-shaped, somewhat similar in appearance to the form of the Central chestnut where these nuts grow three in a bur. The nut is exceedingly variable, not only in size but in form and thinness of shell. Some individual trees bear nuts that are fully six times as large as those borne on other trees from the same lot of seed. The shell is much thinner than that of the Japanese walnut, and the meat is of the same excellent quality. Among all the numerous seedlings of *cordiformis* grown here, nearly every one produced *Sieboldi* trees and nuts, therefore it may as well be understood that cordiformis is only an occasional wide variation from *Sieboldi.*

I speak thus in detail of this variety of the Japanese walnut because its qualities are such as to merit fuller recognition than it has hitherto received. The tree is perhaps as hardy as the

SANTA ROSA WALNUTS

The picture shows the large size of the Santa Rosa walnuts and the symmetrical form and smoothness of the shell. The shell itself is so thin that it can readily be crushed in the fingers.

American black walnut; it is as easily grown, and perhaps even less particular as to soil and climate. The trees are very productive, especially as they grow older. The branches droop under the weight of the nuts. Where other walnut trees bear nuts singly or in clusters of twos or threes, the Japanese walnut tree bears long strings of nuts, sometimes thirty or more in a single cluster. The nuts are thickly set about the axils, the cluster being from six to twelve inches in length.

The meats of the *cordiformis* drop out complete when the thin shells are cracked.

Hybridizing Native Walnuts

The cross between the Persian and Japanese walnuts, like that between the Persian and the California black walnut, did not result in producing a tree that had exceptional value as a nut producer. This cross, like the other, brings together strains that are too widely separated; and while there is a great accentuation of the tendency to growth, so that trees of tremendous size are produced, there is relative sterility, so that a tree sometimes bears only a few individual nuts in a season.

But the results were very strikingly different as regards the matter of bearing when the Cali-

fornia black walnut was hybridized with the
black walnut from the eastern part of the United
States. These two trees are most closely related species, and have diverged relatively little.
Doubtless the time when they had a common ancestor is relatively recent as contrasted with the
period when that common ancestor branched
from the racial stem that bore the Persian and
Japanese walnuts.

Yet the differences between the walnuts of
the eastern and western parts of America are
sufficient to introduce a very strong tendency to
variation.

Indeed, the result of crossing these species
was in some respects scarcely less remarkable
than that due to the crossing of the Persian walnut with the black walnut of California.

In this case, as in the other, the hybrid tree
proved to have extraordinary capacity for
growth. Indeed, I have never been able to decide as to which of the hybrids is the more rapid
grower. But in the matter of nut production,
the discrepancy was nothing less than startling.
For, whereas the first-generation Paradox walnut produced, as we have seen, only occasional
nuts, the hybrid between the two black walnuts—it was named the Royal—proved perhaps
the most productive nut tree ever seen.

I have elsewhere cited a tree sixteen years of age, that produced twenty large apple boxes full of the nuts in a season, so extensive a crop that I sold more than $500 worth of nuts from this single tree that year. And the following year I sold nuts from the same tree to a value of $1,050. The nuts were used for seed to produce trees of the same variety. In 1918 the nuts from this tree were counted and before they had quite all fallen from the tree there were 17,160 nuts making a little over forty-five bushels as they fell in the husk.

This extraordinary difference between the two hybrids is doubtless to be explained by the slightly closer affinity between the parents of the Royal. Their relationship chanced to be precisely close enough to introduce the greatest possible vigor and the largest tendency to variation compatible with fertility. The parents of the Paradox, on the other hand, were removed one stage farther from each other, permitting the production of offspring of vigorous growth, but bringing them near to the condition of infecundity. They were not absolutely sterile, but their fecundity was of a very low order.

The seedlings of the Royal hybrid vary in the second generation, as might be expected,

although the variation in size and foliage is less
than in the case of the Paradox. The extraordinary range of size, some of the second-generation hybrids being giants and others dwarfs,
has been elsewhere referred to. It will be recalled that some of these second-generation hybrids grew to the height of four feet in the first
year, while beside them were others that grew
only six or eight inches and some only one and
one-fourth inch. The nuts from which they
grew had been picked from the same tree, and
planted the same day side by side.

To make sure of securing trees having exactly the traits of the original Royal, it is necessary to grow the trees from grafts either of the
first-generation hybrid or a selected second-generation hybrid showing rapid growth. The number of the latter, however, is sufficient to insure
a reasonable proportion of good trees from any
lot of seed; and the Royal has been in general
demand as a tree to furnish stocks on which
the Persian walnut may be grafted, and for
forestry.

It is found that on most soils a Persian walnut grafted on roots of the Royal hybrid will
produce a much larger crop than if on its own
roots. Moreover the trees under these conditions are relatively free from the blight.

The nuts of the Royal hybrid are similar to those of the parents, except that they are larger in size. The very thick shell is objectionable, as already noted. Doubtless the shell can be made thinner by selective breeding, but no comprehensive efforts in this direction have as yet been carried out. The black walnut, in spite of the really fine quality of its nuts, has never become an important article of commerce. But there are great possibilities for it if the shell could be reduced to a condition comparable to that of the English walnut.

The nuts borne by the Paradox are intermediate in form and appearance between the types of nuts of its parents. Exteriorly they resemble the Persian walnut, but the shell partakes of the thickness and solidity of that of the black walnut. In at least two instances among the thousands of second-generation Paradox walnut trees that have been grown, the trees produce extra large fine walnuts in abundance. However, both of these are quite thick-shelled, but from their second-generation hybrid, which can be multiplied abundantly, good, hardy, thin-shelled varieties may yet be produced.

It is possible that further hybridizations, in which the Royal and Paradox hybrids were themselves crossed, might result in the develop-

ment of a variety, properly selected, that would
retain the good qualities of the Persian nut,
and combine these with the size and prolific bearing of the Royal. This has later been accomplished with striking results.

HYBRIDIZING METHODS

But, of course, whoever undertakes improving
the nut trees must be content to make haste
slowly, for the black walnut has not as yet been
made to bear when very young, as the chestnuts
and some strains of the English walnuts now do.
But in this regard also there would doubtless
be rapid improvement under selection.

The actual method of hand-pollenizing is very
simple. Nothing more is necessary than to break
off the flower-bearing branch, just at the right
time, and shake it over the flowers of the pistillate parent.

Of course, one cannot make sure that some of
the flowers will not be self-fertilized, and this is
wholly unnecessary, for by planting a large
number of the nuts any good judge can determine from the appearance of the seedlings
which ones are hybrids. Also where the trees
grow close together there are sometimes natural
hybrids, though this was not generally known
when I made my first experiments in 1875-1880.

When making these first experiments at hybridizing the walnuts, seeds of the entire tree were planted. In the rows of seedlings, anyone could at once determine which ones were hybridized, as these grew far more rapidly than the others, besides differing notably in general appearance.

First, experiments were made with two black walnuts, and it was the success of this that led me to hybridize the Persian and California walnuts the following year. The hybridization in which the Japanese walnut was used was made a few seasons later. The results, as regards the production of nuts, have been sufficiently detailed. Up to the present no variety of commercial value as a nut bearer has been produced, although the indirect influence of the hybrids on the Persian walnut industry, through their use as stocks, has been quite notable.

THE BUTTERNUTS

There is a very near relative of the black walnut, known as the butternut, that was formerly well known in most forest regions of the eastern United States. The two trees are of closely similar appearance, and the nuts have the same characteristic thick and corrugated shell. The butternut, however, is oval in shape, whereas the

PARENTS AND OFFSPRING

At the right, a specimen of the Persian or English walnut—at the left, a specimen of the Japanese walnut, known as Juglans Seiboldii. In the center a hybrid between these two species. It will be seen that the hybrid is much larger than either parent, and that it shows qualities of each, following the Persian parent in its general appearance, and the Japanese parent in the form of the shell.

walnut is nearly round. The meat of the butternut is also somewhat richer in quality, and it is generally regarded as superior in flavor. The meat itself is by many people regarded as superior to that of any other nut. The difficulty is that the shell, like that of the black walnut, is very thick, making it difficult to extract the meat without breaking it.

The butternut thrives generally where the black walnut does. It makes a more spreading tree, but the wood is softer and far inferior for cabinet purposes.

There is also an Asiatic species, known as *Juglans Manchurica,* that may be regarded as intermediate in form between the butternut and the black walnut. The trees rather closely resemble the Japanese walnut in general appearance, but bear a nut with rough surface like the butternut, and the meat is also similar in quality and appearance to that of the butternut, being superior to that of the black walnut.

This tree may be said to form a connecting link between the Japanese walnut, the American black walnut, and the butternut. Without doubt it could be used advantageously in a hybridizing experiment that would ultimately blend the strains of these different species.

CULTIVATION OF THE WALNUT

The idea of growing walnuts commercially is one that has scarcely been thought of in the temperate regions of the United States. Even in regions of the Middle and Eastern States where the English walnut will grow, it has never been cultivated extensively, and of course this tree is yet too tender to be profitably grown in the colder Northern States. But the black walnut and butternut, on the other hand, are exceedingly hardy trees, thriving even in regions where the winters are excessively cold.

All of these trees, however, require a deep, rich, moist, loamy soil, in order to thrive. Trees that produce wood of such extraordinary hardness of texture, and nuts so stocked with fats and proteins, could not be expected to draw adequate nourishment from impoverished soil. In fact, the black walnut and the butternut, in the regions of the United States to which they are indigenous, are usually found growing along the rivers, or in rich alluvial valleys. The idea that they could be raised to advantage on soil that is too poor to produce ordinary crops of cereals or vegetables is fallacious.

At the moment, there is not demand enough for the black walnut or the butternut to justify the raising of these trees on a commercial scale. It will be necessary to produce new varieties by hybridization and selective breeding before these nuts can be made popular. But, as before said, there is every reason to believe that a series of experiments looking to the production of improved varieties would be more than justified by the results obtained, and I shall point out in another connection the commercial possibilities of producing lumber trees in this way that make the project doubly attractive.

It may be well to call attention to one or two peculiarities of the walnut that should be known to anyone that attempts hybridizing experiments.

In particular it should be understood that the staminate flowers of the walnut usually bloom and shed their pollen from one to four weeks before the fruit-bearing nutlets appear.

One would naturally suppose, under these circumstances, that the pollen would all be lost and that there could be no crop. But the pollen appears to retain its vitality for a long time, and even where it has been shed some weeks before the ripening of the pistillate flowers, there may be a full crop. The hand-pollenizer must bear in mind this tendency of the walnuts to mature their flowers at different times. Still, as already suggested, the pollen appears to retain its vitality, and ultimately to be able to effect fertilization even though applied some time before the full maturity of the pistils.

In parts of France the early spring frosts are likely to be very destructive to the ordinary walnuts, and the French nut raisers have come to depend largely on the Franquette, a variety already referred to. While this variety is in some respects inferior, it has the one supreme quality of not blossoming until the season of spring frosts is over. It blooms perhaps four weeks later than ordinary varieties. This insures a good crop from the Franquette variety, even in years when others have been damaged by frost, so that the average production of this variety throughout a term of years may be higher than that of some others that in any given season may surpass it.

There is opportunity to cross this variety with the other varieties of the Persian walnut that blossom earlier, but produce a better crop of nuts. Such crossing has supplied material from which races have been developed that retain the late-blooming habit of the Franquette, combined with the nut-producing qualities of the other parent.

We have seen that a tendency to bloom late in the season is usually correlative to a tendency to early ripening of fruit, so that late bloomers are adapted to growth relatively far to the north. But this is exactly opposite with the Franquette, this being a late walnut.

But for the production of very hardy races it is probable that hybridizing with the black walnut, the same cross that produced the Paradox, must be looked to, to supply the foundation for a series of experiments in selective breeding.

The pioneer work has been done in the production of the Paradox walnut itself.

It may reasonably be supposed that further experiments, in which this hybrid is used as a parent, will lead to the development of altogether new races of nuts that will have economic importance.

The entire matter of the development of commercial nuts has only recently begun to attract the attention of the growers. There is reason to expect that the developments of the next few generations will be comparable to the progress of the past century in the development of orchard fruits.

THE CHESTNUT — BEARING
NUTS AT SIX MONTHS

A Tree Which Responds to Education

WHEN a boy in Massachusetts, I used to observe the great variation among the native American chestnuts in my father's woodlots. Like most boys I was fond of nuts, and in gathering them soon learned that there were certain trees that bore large, glossy, rich brown nuts with sweet meats, and that there were other trees that bore only small, flat, ash-colored nuts of insignificant size and inferior quality.

I observed that the trees that bore these seemingly quite different nuts differed also in size and in foliage, and particularly noted that such variations were not due to any local conditions, inasmuch as the trees bearing fine nuts and those bearing poor ones might stand side by side.

Similar variations were noted regarding a good many other trees and plants of various kinds. But the variations among the chestnuts,

and also among the pignuts, hazels, hickories,
shellbarks, and butternuts made a very vivid
impression on my mind. It seemed strange that
trees obviously of the same kind should show
such diversity as to their fruit.

When, at a later period, my experiments were
started in California, it occurred to me that a
plant showing such inherent tendency to vary
should afford an unusual opportunity for development—for by this time I had come to fully
appreciate the value of variation as the foundation for the operations of the plant experimenter.

But I had conceived the idea also—as our
earlier studies have shown—that there would be
very great advantage in hybridizing the best
native species of plants with plants of foreign
origin. And the chestnuts were in mind among
others when I sent to Japan and Italy and the
Eastern States for new plants with which to
operate. So the very first lot of plants that came
to me from Japan (in November, 1884),
included twenty-five nuts that I find listed in a
memorandum as "monster" chestnuts. The same
shipment, it may be of interest to recall, included
loquats and persimmons with which some interesting experiments were made; pears, peaches,
and plums of which the reader has already heard;
and climbing blackberries and yellow and red

fruited raspberries that had a share in the development of some fruits that presently attained commercial importance.

But perhaps there was nothing in the entire consignment that was destined to produce seedlings with more interesting possibilities of development than the twenty-five "monster" chestnuts. For the hereditary factors that these nuts bore were to have an important influence in developing new races of chestnuts of strange habits of growth—chestnuts dwarfed to the size of bushes, yet bearing mammoth nuts, and of such precocity of habit as sometimes to begin bearing when only six months from the seed.

To be sure, other chestnut strains were blended with the Japanese before these anomalous results were produced; but it is certain that the oriental parents had a strong influence in determining some at least of the most interesting peculiarities of the new hybrid races.

Very Mixed Ancestry

That the antecedents of the precocious chestnuts may be clearly revealed, let me say at the outset that the Japanese forms were hybridized with the three other species as soon as they were old enough to be mated, and that the hybrids in turn were crossed and recrossed until the strains

SIX-MONTHS-OLD CHESTNUT
TREE IN BEARING

This is a veritable infant prodigy. Only six months ago its cotyledons broke the soil; and to-day it bears good clusters of maturing fruit, as the picture shows. To cause a tree to take on this habit of an annual plant is a remarkable triumph in selective breeding.

had been blended of all the different kinds of chestnuts that could be obtained.

These included, in addition to the Japanese species just cited, representatives of the European chestnut in several of its varieties—one of which came from China—and of the native American chestnut of the familiar type; and also the little native species known as the Chinquapin.

It is interesting to record that the chinquapin, with its almost insignificant nut, crossed readily with the Japanese species, the mammoth nut of which would seem to place it in quite another class.

But there is apparently a very close affinity between all the different chestnuts. All of them have varied and thus perpetuated forms that more or less bridge the gap between the typical representatives of the different species, and, so far as my observations go, all of them may readily be interbred. In a word, the chestnut furnishes most plastic material for the purposes of the plant developer. Just how I have utilized that material will appear as we proceed.

At the time when the chestnuts were received from Japan, there were already at hand trees of the European and American species of various sizes. So soon as the Japanese seedlings were of sufficient size, I grafted them on these European and American trees, in this way being able to stimulate development, and to observe the progress of cions from several hundred seedlings on the same tree.

This, of course, is precisely the method used with my plums and other orchard fruits. The advantages already detailed in connection with the orchard fruits were, of course, found to apply equally to the chestnut. The ingrafted cions were led to fruit much earlier than they would have done on their own roots; there was saving of space; and it was easy to hybridize the many cions that were thus collected on a single tree.

Of course, I was carrying forward numerous experiments with the chestnut all at the same time—crossing each species with every other species, so that in a single season there would be a large number of hybrid forms of different parentage. So when two of the hybrids were interbred the strains of four different species or varieties were blended. Thus a hybrid of the second generation might combine the ancestral strains of the Japanese and European and American chestnuts and of the little chinquapin.

Thus opportunity was made for wide selection among hybrids that combined these various strains in different ways. And for the next generation, I could combine different hybrids or inbreed a given strain or introduce the traits of any different variety chosen.

All these methods were utilized, and in addition, of course, the usual method of rigorous selection was employed, so that soon a colony of chestnuts was developed, not only of the most complicated ancestry, but also a carefully selected colony in which none that did not show exceptional traits of one kind or another had been permitted to remain.

PRECOCIOUS TRAITS

Of the many rather striking peculiarities of the new hybrids, doubtless the one that attracts most general attention is the habit of precocious bearing.

From the outset these hybrids were urged to early bearing, by the method of grafting and selection, as already noted; and of course there were saved for further purposes of experiment only the individuals that were the most precocious, if other good qualities predominated. But, even so, I was not prepared to find some of these seedlings bearing large nuts in abundance in eighteen months from the time of planting the seed. Yet such extraordinary precocity as

YEARLING CHESTNUT TREE IN BEARING

These precocious chestnuts are complex hybrids, combining the traits of European, American, and Japanese ancestors. Such chestnut bushes as this may perhaps take the place of the devastated chestnut forests of our Eastern States.

this was shown by many of the seedlings in the third and subsequent generations.

Moreover, if the grafts were taken from the seedlings and placed on older trees, they would produce nuts within six months after grafting. During the past ten years, many of these seedlings have produced nuts, like annual plants, the first year of planting, while growing on their own roots, and when not over twelve to eighteen inches in height.

The value of such habits of early bearing, from the standpoint of the plant developer, will be obvious. Ordinarily one must expect, in dealing with nut-bearing trees, to wait for a long term of years between generations. In the case of the hickory, for example, after one has planted the nut, it cannot be expected that the seedlings will bear flowers and thus give opportunity for a second hybridizing for at least ten years, and no large crop of nuts may be produced till the tree is forty or fifty years old. So even two or three generations of the hickory compass a large part of a century.

But with these new hybrid chestnuts, generation may succeed generation at intervals of a single year, just as if we were dealing with an annual plant instead of a tree that may live for a century. And of course to this fact very largely I owe the rapid progress of these experiments in the development of new varieties of chestnuts.

Not only do many of the mixed hybrids show this extraordinary precocity, but some of them also develop the tendency to bear continuously. On the same tree throughout most of the year may be found flowers and ripe nuts. Flowers both staminate and pistillate appear on the same tree from time to time, season after season, and in due course the flowers are replaced by growing nuts, so that there is a regular succession month after month.

This habit of continuous bearing, manifested by a tree that ordinarily produces its flowers and in turn its nuts at fixed seasons, is perhaps scarcely less remarkable than the habit of early bearing. Doubtless the two are genetically associated.

Chestnut Seedlings

The care of the chestnut seedlings presents no important complications.

The general plan in selecting seedlings for further tests is the same employed in the selection of seedling fruit trees. Prominent buds, large leaves, thick, heavy twigs, almost invariably forecast large, fine fruit. There is, however, an exception to be noted in the case of the Japanese chestnut, which has smaller leaves. It is necessary to bear this in mind in dealing with seedlings that have a Japanese strain. It is needless to say that the capacity to select the right seedlings for preservation is highly important, as an element in saving time and expense in the practical development of improved varieties of chestnuts.

Already, I have referred to the saving of time that may be accomplished through grafting the chestnut seedlings instead of waiting for them to develop on their own roots. Unlike most other trees, the chestnut should not be grafted until just before the bark begins to slip in the spring. If grafted much earlier it is necessary to protect the grafts by tying a paper sack over them until they start growth to prevent evaporation; but in every case it is better to wait till shortly before the bark begins to slip. This is unlike the cherry, which must be grafted very early or success is extremely doubtful.

When grafting is performed after the bark begins to slip, it is necessary to tie down the bark against the graft with a string to keep it in place, otherwise it rolls away from the graft and union does not take place. If grafting is done at the right time and with reasonable care, it is usually successful.

A SIX-MONTHS-OLD
CHESTNUT TREE

The picture shows the way in which the chestnut burs form in relation to the catkins. Many of the hybrid chestnuts have the peculiar quality of putting forth blossoms at almost every season, so that flower buds and blossoms and mature fruits may be found on the same branch.

In the main, very little attention has been paid to the chestnut by cultivators of nuts. Until very recently, such chestnuts as have appeared in the market have been gathered from wild trees or imported from Europe, Recently, however, the possibilities of cultivating the chestnut have gained attention and in a certain number of cases orchards have been started. I have introduced three different varieties of hybrid chestnuts, the Hale, the Coe, and the McFarland, and these have been grafted on ordinary chestnut stocks to form the basis of many chestnut orchards of the Southern States.

In some cases the roots of the chinquapin have been used as the foundation for grafting, in regions where the ordinary chestnut does not occur. Chestnut orchards have also been started by planting the seed. Reasonable success attends this method, but of course it lacks the certainty of grafting. No one should attempt to start an orchard except by grafting.

Unfortunately there has developed within very recent years a disease that attacks the chestnut tree and invariably destroys it. The disease at first appeared in the neighborhood of New York City about the year 1904, and it has spread in all directions, each year reaching out a little farther, until in 1920 there were very few chestnut trees unscathed within fifty or sixty miles of the original center of contagion.

The cause of the disease is a fungus that is perpetuated by minute spores that are presumably carried through the air and that, when they find lodgment, develop in such a way as to destroy the cambium layer of the bark, presently causing the death of the tree. The small twigs of a single branch will often first show the influence of the fungus and the leaves may die and become brown and shriveled on one or two large limbs of the tree when no other part of it is affected. But in the ensuing season the disease is sure to spread, and the tree seldom survives beyond the third year.

As yet no way of combating the pest has been suggested, except the heroic measure of cutting down trees immediately they are attacked, and burning every portion of their bark. In this way it is hoped to limit somewhat the spread of the disease, but it is by no means sure that the method will be effective. There appears to be danger that the pest will spread until it has decimated the ranks of the chestnut throughout the eastern United States; and of course there is no certainty that it may not find its way to the Pacific Coast, although the lack of chestnut trees in the desert and plateau regions of the Middle West may serve as a barrier.

The precise origin of the fungus that causes the disease was not known until the summer of 1913, when it was discovered by Mr. Frank N. Meyer, of the United States Department of Agriculture, that the fungus (which bears the name *Endothia parasitica*) is indigenous to China. The oriental chestnut trees have become practically immune to it, however, and it does not destroy them, but merely blemishes their bark here and there with canker spots. No one knows just how the disease found its way to the United States, but it may have come on lumber brought from the Orient.

The appearance of this pest came as a very discouraging factor just at a time when interest in the chestnut as a commercial proposition was being thoroughly aroused. Government bulletins had called attention to the value of its nut and its possibility as a paying crop.

But, of course, all expectations were nullified in the regions where the ravages of the chestnut fungus are felt.

Fortunately, it appears that some of the hybrid races that bear the oriental strain are immune to the disease. Reports show that hybrids between the Japanese chestnut and the

BUR AND CATKIN

It always seems matter for surprise that the round burs of the chestnut should grow in catkins that seemed destined to produce fruit clusters of a quite different type. Here is a picture that emphasizes the contrast, as it shows a well-developed bur in connection with the remains of the catkin.

American chinquapin are peculiarly resistant. The chinquapin itself is at least partially immune to the disease, but of course this tree bears a nut that is too small to have commercial value. The hybrids, however, in some cases are said to retain the good qualities of the chestnut tree combined with the capacity to bear large nuts acquired from their oriental ancestor.

It is obvious, then, that here is another case in which the introduction of new blood from the Orient may be of inestimable value. The loss of our native chestnuts is a calamity, but it is a calamity that is not irreparable. We may have full assurance that new chestnut groves will spring up in the wake of the pest.

It is obvious that the early-bearing chestnut offers great advantages for such reforestation. The probability that these will prove immune to the pest gives them added attractiveness. If, however, the existing varieties should prove not to be immune, it will be necessary to develop resistant varieties. For it is obvious that the cultivation of the chestnut will not be abandoned merely because it has met with an unexpected setback.

It has already been pointed out that the chestnut has exceptional food value on account of its high percentage of starchy matter. It therefore occupies a place in the dietary that is not held by any other nut. So there is an exceptional incentive to reintroduce the trees in devastated regions.

THE CHESTNUT ORCHARD

Possibly the coming of the chestnut plague, even though it has resulted directly in the destruction of the entire chestnut groves throughout wide regions, may be a blessing in disguise, as it may make it necessary to bring the chestnut under cultivation in order to preserve the nut at all, whereas in the past it has grown so abundantly in the wild that little attention has been paid to it.

Accounts of the destruction of the trees have doubtless brought the chestnut to the attention of many people who hitherto have never given it a thought. The value of the chestnut as an ornamental tree and its possibilities as a nut producer will perhaps be more fully appreciated than they otherwise would be on the familiar principle that blessings brighten as they take their flight. And it may chance that the tree will be placed under cultivation so generally as to be more abundant twenty-five or thirty years from now in the devastated regions than it would have been if the chestnut blight had not appeared.

In any event it seems now at least as desirable as ever before to urge the value of this tree both for ornamental purposes and as a producer of commercial nuts, and the rules for the development of chestnut orchards that have been given by the Department of Agriculture may be reviewed to advantage.

Even if people living in the infected district are slow to take up the cultivation of the chestnut, the orchardists of other regions may advantageously do so. For it is not supposable that the coming of a fungoid pest will be permitted to exterminate one of our most valuable native trees.

In developing a commercial chestnut orchard it is obviously desirable to graft with the improved varieties. Quite aside from the matter of producing trees that are immune to the fungous pest, the orchard may be made far more productive if grafted with improved varieties than if the native species were used.

Some of these seedlings, for example, produce nuts two inches in diameter, each weighing an ounce or more; and these are borne in clusters of from six to nine nuts to the bur. It is notable, however, that the excessively large nuts are usually lacking in flavor; although the reasonably large ones are of the best quality.

WELL PROTECTED

Most of the hybrid chestnuts have a spiny covering that affords ample protection against the attacks of birds or squirrels. In this regard, the specimen here shown resembles the typical chestnuts of our eastern forests. There are other varieties, however, that have given up their spiny covering, leaving the burs as smooth as apples.

These hybrid varieties graft readily on the native stock. They may be counted on to bear abundantly the second season. It may be well, however, to pick off the burs as soon as formed during the first year or two, in order that the energies of the tree may be given over to the production of branches.

Even where the blight has destroyed the chestnut, the sprouts that spring up everywhere about the stumps of the trees may be grafted and trees of more satisfactory qualities than the old ones and far more productive may thus be developed in the course of a few years.

Where the chestnut orchard is developed from the seed or by transplanting seedlings, it is recommended that it should be located on a well-drained sandy or gravelly soil. The trees thrive well on rocky hillsides, and even on rather poor sand, but observation has shown that they are somewhat uncertain of growth on stiff clay soils in the east, although Italian chestnuts in California are said to thrive on heavy clays. In general, it is more important to have a thoroughly drained soil than soil of a particular character.

It will be recalled that my new varieties were developed on the foundation of stocks imported from Japan. It will also be understood, as a matter of course, that selections with this tree as with all other plants have been made always with an eye to the exclusion of any races that showed susceptibility to fungous pests of any kind.

As an illustration of the care with which these selections were made, in the development of the improved varieties, I may note that in various instances only three or four seedlings were selected out of ten thousand. It may be added that orchards made by grafting cions of these improved hybrid chestnuts on ordinary American stock have proved enormously productive.

It has been estimated that rocky and otherwise useless hillsides may be made productive, where practically nothing else could be grown that would be of special value.

This western golden chestnut (*Castanea chrysophylla*) is a remarkable species. On the heights of the Sierra Nevada mountains it grows as a shrub only four or five feet tall, much branched. These shrubs produce nuts quite abundantly. Along the coast the same species grows to a height of 150 feet, with an immense trunk. One can scarcely believe that the little bush and the gigantic tree are of the same species.

Being an unusually ornamental evergreen the mountain variety should be extensively planted in cold climates.

There is a great difference among the different chestnuts as to the amount of their sugar content. In some species the starch is so little transformed that the nuts are scarcely edible unless cooked. In others there is an abundant sugar content, the nuts being sweet and palatable. Of course this matter was in mind in developing hybrid varieties. But there is still opportunity for improvement.

It is also desirable to reduce the amount of tannin contained in nearly all of the varieties.

Some of the chinquapin varieties also have the habit of holding the leaves during the winter, giving the trees a very untidy appearance. Seedlings that show this tendency should be avoided in making selection.

POINTS IN SELECTION

Of course it is elementary to say that the nuts should be selected for dark, rich, glossy brown color, for tenderness of flesh, and for productiveness. Of my three earlier introduced varieties, all were early and abundant bearers, but one was particularly notable for its earliness, and another for its combination of good qualities.

Doubtless the feature that is next in line of improvement in the development of the chestnut

CHESTNUTS IN THE BUR

In this specimen, as will be seen, the spiny covering is relatively reduced, as compared with the bulk of the nuts within the bur. Contrast this specimen, with regard to its spiny covering, with the specimens shown in the preceding pictures.

is the bur itself. A few of these hybrid seedlings were wholly spineless, the covering being
as smooth as that of the walnut. In the wild
state, the chestnut needs a spiny bur to protect
it from squirrels and birds. It has developed this
protective covering through natural selection,
just as the walnut has developed its thick coat
filled with bitter astringent juices.

The new partially spineless varieties have been
developed merely by selection from a hybrid seedling that produced nuts showing a tendency to
have fewer spines than ordinarily. Of course the
tendency to vary in this regard was accentuated
by hybridization as were other tendencies. Or,
stated otherwise and a little more technically, the
hybridization has made possible the segregation
of hereditary characteristics, bringing to the surface factors for spinelessness that no doubt have
been transmitted as recessive traits for perhaps
thousands of generations.

No doubt difficulties will be involved in perfecting a race of chestnuts with smooth burs
similar to those that attend the development of
the thornless blackberry and the spineless cactus. But there is reason to expect that the same
measure of success will be attained with the
chestnut that was attained with the other spine
bearers.

A nut that combines all the good qualities of the hybrid early-bearing chestnuts and in addition is borne in a spineless bur would have a combination of qualities that should appeal to the orchardist, and doubtless will do so when the idea that chestnuts may form valuable commercial crops gains wider appreciation.

THE HICKORY NUT — AND
OTHER NUTS

Improvements Which Have Been Made
and Some Suggestions

THERE is perhaps no other wild plant producing a really delicious food product that has been so totally neglected by the cultivator as the shagbark or shellbark hickory tree (*Carya ovata*).

The better varieties of hickory nuts always find a ready sale in the market, and are highly prized by the housekeeper. But such nuts as find their way to the market are almost without any exception the product of wild trees, gathered usually by some wandering boy, and often regarded as the property of whoever can secure them, regardless of the ownership of the land on which the tree grows.

Even the new interest in nuts as food products and as orchard crops that has been developed in our own generation, has hardly as yet included the hickory, or at least has not sufficed to bring the hickory tree from the woods and give it a place within the territory of the orchardist.

The reason for this, doubtless, is that the hickory is a tree of very slow growth, and that it is also exceedingly difficult to propagate by budding or grafting, or any other process except from the seed.

The prospect of improving the product of a tree that does not bear until it is ten or fifteen years old, and that resists all efforts to force it to early bearing, is not alluring, considering the short span of human life. Yet we can scarcely doubt that the hickory nut will soon be brought within the ken of the plant experimenter, and that there will ultimately be developed nuts of very choice varieties, comparable in size, probably, to the English walnut, and having a quality that will place them at least on a par with any other nut now grown in the temperate zones.

Even in the wild state the best of shellbark hickories bear nuts of unchallenged quality. It is a matter of course that these nuts can be improved by cultivation and selective breeding.

Material for such selective breeding is furnished abundantly by the wide variation of hickories in the wild state. I had observed this variation in my boyhood days, just as I had noted the variation in the chestnuts. The shagbark hickory, doubtless the best of the tribe, was quite abundant along the banks of the Nashua River near my home, and I early learned to distinguish the great difference in the products of the trees, all of which, of course, were natural seedlings.

Among hundreds of trees there would be scarcely two that bore nuts of precisely the same appearance and quality.

Some of these hickory nuts were long and slender, with prominent ridges; some were short and compact and smooth in contour; some were very flat and others were nearly globular. The shell varied correspondingly in thickness, and the meat varied greatly in whiteness and in flavor.

As a boy I knew very well which trees to seek in the fall in order to secure nuts that were plump and thin-shelled, with sweet and delicious meats. It was only after the crop of these trees had been gathered that inferior ones gained attention.

I knew very well, also, that different trees varied greatly in productiveness, some bearing nuts so abundantly each year that the ground was literally covered when the nuts fell. Others produced nuts very sparingly.

The trees that thus varied as to their fruit, varied also in form, in size, and in rapidity of growth. In a word, the wild hickories repre-sented numerous varieties that a boy could differ-

HICKORY NUTS

There is marked variation in the size, form, and quality of the nuts of different hickory trees, even when growing in the same neighborhood. Thus there is good opportunity for selective breeding, but unfortunately the hickory is of such slow growth that few experimenters have the courage to undertake its development. The hickory does not ordinarily bear nuts until it is ten or twelve years old.

entiate, whether or not a botanist might choose to classify them as members of the same species.

All these varied members of the shagbark tribe bear nuts that have an unmistakable individuality of flavor that distinguishes them from any other nuts. Much as they varied in size and degrees of excellence, all of them were hickory nuts, and could be mistaken for nothing else. There were, however, other hickory trees growing in equal abundance on my father's place, though they differed essentially in appearance from the shagbark nuts, that produced nuts of a far less interesting character.

Hickories of this kind were locally called pignuts. They are classified by the botanist as *Hicoria glabra,* or *Carya glabra.*

The trees of this species are more upright and symmetrical, and of much more rapid growth than the shagbark. The nut has a thin husklike outer cover and a rather thick shell, and the meat is difficult to remove, and is so ill-flavored that it is little prized by anyone. Indeed, the nuts are usually not gathered at all if shagbark hickories of any quality can be obtained.

Nevertheless, there was great diversity among the pignuts no less than among the hickories of the better species. So with these also there is doubtless opportunity of improvement through selective breeding, although up to the present time few comprehensive experiments in this direction have been made.

I have now little doubt that some of the variant hickories that I knew as a boy were hybrids.

The two species of hickory are closely related and I have reason to believe hybridize sometimes in the wild state. I have received specimens of hickory nuts from different parts of the United States that certainly were natural hybrids and no doubt such hybridization occurs not infrequently. The hickory and the pecan also cross quite readily.

It is probable that when the attempt is systematically made to develop the hickory nut, the method of hybridizing the various species will be employed to give still wider variation and to facilitate a wider selection.

SOME ENORMOUS WESTERN HICKORIES

There is a species of the hickory nut (*C. laciniosa*) that grows in the valleys of the Mississippi and the Ohio that is of relatively enormous size. The shell of this variety, however, is thick, and the meat is not generally as fine in flavor as that of the eastern shellbark hickory. But the size of this wild variety gives assurance that under cultivation and selection the nut may be made to take on proportions that will be very attractive. Doubtless the comparatively small size of the wild hickory nut has led to its neglect, although we must recall that the walnut and the butternut have also been neglected, notwithstanding their much larger size.

The chief reason why these nuts have been overlooked, doubtless, is that the idea of making nuts a cultivated crop, comparable to orchard fruits, has only recently been conceived in America—or at all events has only recently been given general recognition.

There is reason to expect that the next generation will see somewhat the same rapid progress in the art of developing the nut-bearing trees that has been witnessed in the past three or four in the development of orchard fruits. And certainly the hickory nut, walnut, and butternut constitute better native material than the wild plums, for example, with the aid of which some of the finest varieties of cultivated plums have been developed within most recent years.

And it must not be forgotten that the work of developing our native nuts has already passed the experimental stage with regard to at least one species. This is the nearest relative of the hickory, a member of the same genus, which is familiar as the pecan.

A PECAN TREE

The pecan is closely related to the hickory, but is a much less hardy tree, being confined to the Southern States. It sometimes hybridizes with the hickory in the wild state, and it is possible that new and hardy varieties of nuts might be produced by selection among the progeny of such a cross. The pecan is rapidly assuming great importance as a commercial nut.

This nut grows only in the southern parts of the United States, being far less hardy than the other hickories. But what it lacks in hardiness it makes up in quality, and it is pretty generally regarded as the best nut that is grown in temperate climates, not even excepting the English walnut.

The relationship between the northern hickories and the pecan is attested by the fact that in the regions where the two tribes intermingle, they hybridize freely.

I have received specimens of the nuts that were undoubtedly hybrids between the shagbark hickory and the pecan, and these included two or three varieties that are among the finest nuts that I have ever seen. Great improvements in the pecan may result from hybridizing this nut with the shagbark hickory.

THE CULTIVATION OF THE PECAN

Even in its existing varieties, however, the pecan nut has most attractive qualities; and it has the distinction of being the only native nut that has hitherto been placed under cultivation on an extensive scale and has attained commercial importance.

We have already referred to the economic importance of this nut in an earlier chapter, and mention was there made of the fact that all the pecans now under cultivation are directly derived from a few wild varieties that have been propagated by budding and grafting. It is only in recent years that a method of grafting this nut successfully has been developed, and as yet little or nothing has been done toward improving the wild varieties.

The fact that the nut in its wild state has such attractive qualities gives full assurance that under cultivation and development it will prove of even greater value.

In selecting the best wild varieties for cultivation, attention has been paid to the matter of early bearing, and in particular to persistent bearing. So the orchards that have recently been started are stocked with trees that may be expected to bear crops of nuts in about seven or eight years, and that may be depended on to produce a crop each year with reasonable certainty. But as to both time of bearing and regularity and abundance of production, there is still opportunity for much improvement.

Doubtless improved varieties may be secured through mere selection by raising seedlings from the nuts grown on trees that were especially good bearers. But it is probable, also, that the full possibility of the pecan will not be realized until extensive series of crossing experiments have been carried out.

Hitherto, no extensive experiments in hybridizing the various species and varieties have been carried out, although it is barely possible that some of the wild varieties of pecans that have been brought into the orchard were natural hybrids.

It is to be hoped that experiments along this line will be taken up in the near future, but, of course, many years will be required before notable results can be attained.

It is desirable, also, to cross the pecan with the Japanese walnut. If hybridization could be effected, it may be expected that trees of rapid growth, similar to my hybrid walnuts, will be produced. Not unlikely some varieties that tend to produce nuts at a very early age, like my hybrid chestnuts, may also appear as the result of such combinations. And in any event it may confidently be expected that new varieties will give opportunity for wide selection, and for relatively rapid improvement in the qualities of the nuts themselves.

We have learned that the preeminent qualities of our various cultivated fruits have largely been given them by natural and artificial crossing.

A VARIETY OF TROPICAL NUTS

Here are a few specimens among the many tropical nuts with which we chance to be experimenting at the present time. Just what will come of these experiments it is not possible to predict.

The contrast between the tiny beach plum, for example, and its gigantic descendant a few generations removed, offers an object lesson in the possibilities of fruit development by crossing and selection. And, for that matter, each and every one of our improved varieties of orchard fruits teaches the same lesson, even though the wild progenitor is not at hand for comparison.

So there is every reason to expect that the wild pecan will similarly respond to the efforts of the plant developer, and that its descendants, a few generations removed, will take on qualities that even the most sanguine experimenter of to-day would scarcely dare to predict.

One improvement that might probably be secured without great difficulty is the introduction of the quality of hardiness, so that the pecan might be cultivated farther to the north. At present the pecan does not produce profitably as a rule, even in the coast counties of California, as the nights are too cool, thus making the season too short for the pecan to ripen its fruit. About Vacaville they thrive much better, and the Sacramento and San Joaquin Valleys, where the nights are very warm, there is as good prospect of growing the pecan profitably as anywhere else in the world. But in the main the cultivation of this nut has hitherto been restricted to the region of the Gulf of Mexico. It is obviously desirable that so valuable a nut should be adapted to growth in wider territories.

The fact that the pecan will hybridize with the hardy hickory obviously points the way to the method through which this end may be attained.

The peculiarity of the hickory and pecan that is associated with their long life and slow growth, is the fact that during their first year the seedlings make perhaps 99 per cent of their growth under ground. They produce enormous roots before they make any appreciable growth above ground.

It is not unusual to find pecan seedlings an inch high with roots from four to six feet in length, and an inch in diameter at the widest part.

Such a root system prepares the tree for the strong growth that characterizes it later; but a seedling that makes only a few inches of growth in the first season is a rather discouraging plant from the standpoint of the cultivator. Doubtless the pecan may be induced to change its habit in this regard by hybridizing. The example of the hybrid walnuts may be cited as showing that a tree that is ordinarily slow of growth may be made to take on the habit of very rapid growth without relinquishing any of its other characteristics of hardiness and the production of valuable timber.

The case of the Royal walnut shows also that the tree that thus becomes a rapid grower may also have the habit of enormous productivity.

If the pecan could similarly be stimulated to increased rapidity of growth, and to a proportionate capacity for nut bearing, this tree would be a fortune-maker for the orchardist. And there is no obvious reason why the pecan should not have the same possibilities of development that have been demonstrated to be part of the endowment of its not very distant relative, the walnut.

FILBERTS AND HAZELNUTS

There is yet another native American nut as hardy and as widespread as the hickory, that has been even more persistently neglected. This is the familiar hazelnut.

There are two familiar types of hazelnut that often grow in the same region, and that resemble each other so closely that the boys who gather the nuts commonly do not discriminate between them. One of these grows in husks with a long beak, while the other has an incurved husk that in some cases does not fully cover the nuts. There are sundry varieties of the two species that may sometimes be found growing in the same patch.

CHINQUAPINS AND CHESTNUTS

The chinquapin is a species of chestnut bearing very small nuts, which have, however, the typical chestnut form and quality. The picture, showing chinquapins at the top and dwarf hybrid chestnuts below, illustrates both the similarity in form and the contrast in size. The strains of the chinquapin have been combined with those of the other chestnuts in our complex hybrids.

The fact of such variation in the wild species is of course important from the standpoint of the plant developer. We have learned from frequent repetition that where there is variation there is opportunity for selection and improvement.

The hazelnut has a European relative that is familiar in America as the filbert. This is merely a larger hazelnut, the qualities of the two nuts both as to form and flavor being such as to leave no question of their relationship. But for some reason the European nut appears not to thrive in this country. At all events it has never been cultivated here on a commercial scale.

But for that matter the hazelnut has never been cultivated on a scale commercial or otherwise, unless in the most exceptional instances when it has been brought into the garden by some one rather as a curiosity than for any commercial purpose. Yet the nut is a really valuable one, and certainly it is one that may repay cultivation and development.

Attempts have been made to grow the European filbert in Sonoma County, California, both from seed and from division, but in all cases these attempts have failed. The purple-leafed hazelnut grows and thrives here in California as it does almost everywhere else in the United States.

The species known as *Corylus rostrata* grows
wild rather abundantly in certain sections, but
it is a shy bearer.

There is no obvious reason why the European
filbert should not be cultivated in this country
if a study is made of its needs as to soil and climate. Also, there is no apparent reason why it
should not be crossed with the American hazelnut. The result of such crossing, if we may draw
inferences from analogy, would be the production of a race of hazel-filberts of greatly increased
size, and of improved quality.

There is a so-called filbert, or Chilean hazelnut,
that grows in South America. This plant bears
a nut similar to the filbert, but very much larger
in size and of far better quality. It is difficult,
however, to get a start in the cultivation of this
plant, as its seeds when brought to this country
ordinarily do not germinate. I have at last succeeded, however, in producing several young
trees. This is a beautiful evergreen tree, and
should prove of great value. In its own country
the young trees are highly prized, selling for a
large sum when only a few inches high.

The European filbert grows readily from the
seed, but does not by any means come true. Indeed, it proves exceedingly variable. But this,
of course, from the standpoint of the plant de-

veloper could not be regarded as a fault. If through selective breeding a variety could be produced that would bear regularly and abundantly, and in particular if the size of the nuts was increased, this would be one of the most important of all nuts. As yet, however, a variety that is adapted to growth in this country has not been produced.

SOME FOREIGN POSSIBILITIES

A nut that has come to be fairly well known in the market in recent years, but which has hitherto scarcely been grown in this country, is the Pistachio. The tree on which this nut grows is a member of the sumac family. The nuts are small, but on the best trees are produced in profusion.

In recent years the Department of Agriculture of the United States Government has imported a great number of plants and seeds of the pistachio, which are now being grown experimentally, and which, it is hoped, will form the basis of an extensive culture of this nut. The experiment has not as yet progressed far enough to make predictions possible as to the results. My own experience with the nut is limited to the growing of a few plants about thirty-five years ago, which, after they had been cultivated for a dozen years or more were found not to be a fruiting variety, and so were destroyed.

An Australian tree-shrub, a small tree called the *Macadamia ternifolia,* has been introduced in California in recent years, and is regarded as a valuable acquisition. The tree is ornamental, and bears a fruit that is regarded as of value. At the center of the fruit is a round, delicious nut, much larger than the ordinary filbert, sometimes almost equaling a small English walnut, that is fully equal in flavor to the best filbert or almond.

The *Macadamia* has proved hardy in this vicinity, but requires a well-drained soil. A wet winter is very destructive to the trees, unless they are on dry, well-drained land.

There are several species of *Macadamia,* the one that I have raised most extensively being known as *Macadamia ternifolia.* This is a handsome evergreen, the leaves of which resemble those of the magnolia, but are thinner and rougher. The nuts are often an inch in diameter, with rather thin but hard shells, and large, round, delicious meats. Further tests will be necessary before the climatic limitations of the *Macadamia* are fully established. But in regions where it can be grown, it must prove a nut of great value.

GROWING TREES FOR LUMBER

PROFITABLE FORESTRY

MANY years ago I had a talk with an official connected with the Department of Forestry, at Washington, in which I suggested that the problems of his department could best be met by the development of new types of forest trees.

The official regarded the suggestion as grotesque. In common with nearly everyone else at that time he looked upon the tree as a fixed product of nature, quite beyond the possibilities of any change that man could direct.

There was a time when Darwinism, although it had pretty fully established itself in the scientific world, was still on trial in the minds of the people in general. And even those who accepted the general truth of the Darwinian doctrine of evolution for the most part did not realize that evolution is a process that is going on about us

97

to-day along the same lines that have characterized it in the past.

To accept the doctrine of evolution at all required the overturning of the most fundamental
ideas. After the conception had been grasped
that in the past there had been eras of change
and development, it was a long time before even
the most imaginative scientist fully grasped the
notion that our age also is a time of change and
transition, and that the metamorphoses of plants
and animals through which new forms have
evolved in the past are being duplicated under
our eyes in our own time. And in particular, as
regards so massive and seemingly stable a structure as the tree, was it peculiarly difficult for
botanists to conceive of flexibility and propensity
to change, or to evolve, in the present time.

It is true that no very keen observation was
required to see that trees differ among themselves within the same species, but it is also true
that these divergences always fall within certain
limits and that on the whole they may be regarded as insignificant when weighed in the
balance against numberless characteristics in
regard to which the trees of a species seem
practically identical.

Take, for example, all the individuals that one
could observe of, let us say, the common shag-

bark hickory, the variations of which were referred to in the preceding chapter. Attention was called to the fact that the hickories observed as a boy in the neighborhood of my New England home differed in size and form, and that the nuts that they bore were sometimes oval, sometimes rounded in form, sometimes rough, sometimes smooth, sometimes thick, and sometimes thin of shell, and equally diversified as to the quality of their meat. But of course I should be foremost to admit that all these diversities were in the aggregate of minor significance in comparison with the characteristics that even the most divergent of the hickories had in common each with all the rest. All were trees that attained a fair size as trees go.

All have roots and trunks and branches of the same general form and aspect—as much alike, for example, as the bodies and arms and legs of human beings.

All of them had leaves that could at once be distinguished as being leaves of the hickory and of no other tree.

All had bark with the same characteristic whitish color and the same tendency to scale off in layers; and although the bark of some was much rougher than that of others, any fragment of bark of any hickory tree could readily enough be distinguished as characteristic of the species, and as not by any chance having grown on any other kind of tree.

Then, too, if the hickory tree were felled and cut into firewood, the texture and fiber of the wood itself enabled anyone who glanced at it to pronounce it hickory as definitely and with as much certitude as if he had seen the tree while living and in full leaf. No other wood had quite the same whiteness as the pignut hickory, or quite the same strength and elasticity of fiber.

The Indians had learned this in the old days, and had used the hickory of a preference always in making their bows.

We boys, in our barbaric age, followed the Indian's example. We knew that a bow of hickory had elastic qualities that no other bow could hope to match.

All in all, then, the hickory, despite the trivialities of variation which are mentioned in the preceding chapter, stands apart when we come to examine it comprehensively, as a tree differing from all others and obviously entitled to stand as a unified and differentiated genus.

And what is true of the hickory is no less true of each and every species of tree in our forest. Each walnut and oak and beech and birch and pine and linden and locust has a thousand points of unison with every other member of its own species, could we analyze its characteristics in detail, for every conspicuous point of divergence. If we consider minutiæ of detail as to size and exact form of leaf and all the rest, no two individuals are identical. But if, on the other hand, we take the broad view, it is clear that each recognized species stands out in a place apart, grouped with all the other members of its own kind, and somewhat isolated from all other species.

Such being the obvious fact, it was perhaps not strange that the botanists and foresters of twenty-five years ago looked almost with suspicion on anyone who suggested that the different species of forest trees might be interbred and modified and used as material for building of new species that would better fulfill the conditions of reforestation than any existing species. Even botanists who thought that they fully grasped the idea of Darwinian evolution looked askance at such a suggestion.

It seemed to bid defiance to the laws of heredity, as they understood them.

It appeared almost like an affront to Nature herself to suggest that her handiwork might thus be modified and improved.

MATERIALS FOR SELECTION

And it may well be questioned whether this point of view would have been altered even to this day had it not been for a conspicuous and notable demonstration of the possibility of modifying existing species of trees.

The demonstration was made when I took pollen from the flower of a Persian walnut and transferred it to the pistils of the California black walnut.

Here were two species of trees so notably different in form and shape of leaf and fruit and color of wood that not even the most casual observer could confound them. They were not even natives of the same continent, and no botanist would claim that they were as closely related as are many species of forest trees that grow side by side in our woodlands and maintain unchallenged their specific identity.

Yet when these two trees were cross-pollenized they produced fertile nuts, and trees of a new order grew from these fertile seeds.

The barriers between these not very closely related species were broken down, and a new type of forest tree was produced that differed so markedly from either parent that no one could confound it with either, and that excelled both in the capacity for rapid growth so conspicuously as to seem to belong not merely to a different species but to an entirely different tribe of trees.

Here it is referred to only in connection with the demonstration it gave of the possibility that new types of forest trees might be developed by hybridization and selection, quite as had been claimed in the comment that aroused such skeptical and even sarcastic response from the professional forester.

But after this demonstration had been made it was no longer possible even for the hidebound conservative to deny the possibility that forest trees, like other plants, are somewhat plastic materials in the hands of the plant developer.

And in course of time it came to be recognized—though even now the knowledge has scarcely been acted on—that the new idea given by observation of the Royal and Paradox walnuts could be utilized for the practical purpose of supplying timber trees that might be expected to restock our woodland in a fraction of the time that would be required for the growing of trees of unmodified wild species.

The row of Paradox walnut trees which at fifteen years of age were two feet in diameter

THE WILD NUTMEG

The nutmegs belong to the genus Myristica. They are mostly tropical plants and must be cultivated under glass if grown in northern regions. This is a handsome evergreen, rare even in California. It is in no way related to the tropical nutmeg except in the appearance of the fruit.

and towered as beautiful and symmetrical trees to the height of sixty feet, standing just across the street from their Persian parent, which at thirty-two years of age was nine inches in diameter and perhaps forty feet high, afforded an object lesson that even the most skeptical could not ignore.

The Royal and Paradox hybrids and their fellows must be called upon to restock the ravaged timber lands of America. New hybrids must be produced by the union of varied species of pines, oaks, and elms, and other timber and ornamental trees, to give diversity to the landscape and to supply different types of wood for the uses of carpenter and cabinet-maker.

The Royal and Paradox walnuts—as the working model for a new order of mechanism—a timber tree that shall be able to reforest a treeless region in half a human generation with a growth ready for the ax and saw of the lumberman.

The Materials at Hand

In preparing this new material for the making of forest trees, it will be possible, no doubt, to bring trees from foreign lands, either for direct transplantation or as hybridizing agents.

Thus, as we have seen, one of the parents of the Paradox walnut was a tree not indigenous to America. But we may recall also that another hybrid walnut, the Royal, which sprang from the union of two indigenous species, the black walnut of the eastern United States and the black walnut of California, rivals the Paradox in its capacity for rapid and gigantic growth.

So it is obvious that we are by no means reduced to the necessity of making requisition on foreign lands for material with which to develop our new races of quick-growing forest trees.

But, on the other hand, the plant developer is always willing to take his own where he finds it. So if foreign species can be found that will hybridize advantageously with our native species, they will of course be welcomed. The reader will recall that I have invoked the aid of numberless exotic fruit trees and vegetables and flower bearers in the course of experiments in plant development.

In some cases it will be possible to bring the foreign species and acclimate them without hybridization. This has been done with several species of eucalyptus and acacias which have been brought to California from Australia and have proved a wonderful addition to the ranks of our ornamental and timber trees.

Everyone who visits California marvels at the eucalyptus, and those of us who watch it year after year marvel equally, because this tree has capacity for growth that seems little less than magical. No other trees, perhaps, ever seen in America, with the exception of the hybrid walnuts, have such capacity to add to their stature and girth year by year as has the eucalyptus.

Moreover the eucalyptus may be cut for timber, its trunk severed only a few inches above the ground; and it will send forth shoots that dart into the air and transform themselves into new trunks, each seeming to strive to rival the old one. From the roots of the fallen giant spring a galaxy of new giants, and each new shoot assumes the proportions of a tree with almost unbelievable celerity.

Add that the wood of the eucalyptus, notwithstanding its rapid growth, is among the hardest, and the remarkable character of this importation from the Southern Hemisphere will be more clearly realized.

Unfortunately the eucalyptus is sensitive to cold; otherwise it would at once offer a solution of the problem of reforestation throughout the whole of the United States.

Perhaps the eucalyptus may be made more hardy by hybridizing and selection. At least we

must heed the lessons it gives—in common with
the hybrid walnuts—as to the possibility that a
tree may show almost abnormal capacity for
rapid growth and at the the same time may produce lumber of the hardest texture.

Hitherto it has generally been supposed that
a tree of rapid growth would as a matter of
course produce soft timber. The hybrid walnuts and the various eucalyptus trees serve to
dispel that fallacy.

NATIVE MATERIALS

The one fault of the eucalyptus, its inability
to stand extreme cold, is likely to be shared by
other trees that are imported from the subtropical regions of our own hemisphere.

Although, as just suggested, it may be possible
to overcome this fault through selective breeding, a long series of experiments will doubtless
be necessary before this can be accomplished.
In the meantime we shall be obliged to place
chief dependence, in all probability, upon our
native stock of trees, hybridized perhaps with
allied species of Europe and northern Asia.

But, even so, there is no dearth of material.
America is richly stocked with forest trees.
Moreover these represent, so the geological
botanists assure us, a flora of very ancient origin

which has shown its capacity to maintain itself through successive eras during which there have been tremendous climatic changes.

It follows that our native forest trees have in their heredity the reminiscence of many and widely varying environments. And by the same token they have capacity for variation, and therefore afford exceptional opportunity for diversified development.

It is not necessary here to analyze in great detail the qualities of the different groups of forest trees. A brief summary of the characteristics of a few of the more important groups will serve to suggest the abundance of native material, and to give at least an inkling as to what may be expected, in the light of what was revealed by the experiments with the walnuts, as to possibilities of development of the different tribes.

Of course the great family of cone bearers stands in the foreground, represented by many species, and known as the timber trees that give us the the pine lumber which has everywhere been the chief material for the carpenter, and an important foundation material for the cabinet-maker.

We have but to recall the giant sequoias of California, the largest trees existing anywhere in

the world, to be made aware of the possibilities
of growth that are present in the racial strains of
the family of cone bearers. And even if these
giants shall be regarded as representatives of an
antique order that outlived its era, there remain
numerous pines and firs and hemlocks of magnificent proportions to test the skill of the plant
developer for their betterment and there is
every probability that the coast redwood and the
Sierra big tree may be crossed, and a variety
produced that will be adapted to new conditions
and which will outgrow all other trees.

Nothing could be easier than to cross-pollen-
ize members of this tribe, inasmuch as the pollen
is produced in the utmost profusion, and the
pistillate flowers are exposed when mature in
the nascent cones awaiting fructification. That
cross-fertilization occurs among the wild trees
through the agency of the wind is a matter of
course. Doubtless there are hybrid species of
pines and their allies, everywhere often unrecog-
nized or classified as good species. Quite large
forests mostly composed of hybrid cypresses are
found in California, and the oaks are known to
hybridize frequently; also the eucalyptus trees
of various species.

If study were made of individual conifers in
any forest region where different species are

found, it would doubtless be possible to secure by mere selection new races that would admirably serve the purposes of the forester.

But of course still better results may be expected when pollenizing is carried out intelligently, and the racial strains of different species of conifers are blended and tested to find just what are the best combinations.

It would not be strange if among the hybrids there should be found one or more varieties that will attempt to rival the *Sequoia* itself in giantism, and that will quite outrival it in rapidity of growth.

What the pines are as producers of white and relatively soft wood of straight grain and uniform texture, the members of the great family of oaks are as producers of wood of hard texture, irregularly grained and knotted, but capable of taking on a polish and serving almost every essential purpose of the cabinetmaker.

The most famous of oaks, doubtless, is the typical British species, but the American white oak is a close second. Perhaps these two might be hybridized. If the hybrid thus produced were by any chance to show the capacity for rapid growth that the hybrid walnuts have shown, while retaining the hardness of texture of its parents, as the hybrid walnuts do, the tree thus produced

would by itself go far toward solving the problem of reforestation. The oaks quite frequently
hybridize in a state of nature.

Granted a producer of soft white wood such as
probably can be made by combining the white
pine with some of its allies; a producer of hard
cabinet wood such as a hybrid between the
British oak and the American white oak would
probably constitute; and the hybrid walnuts
already in existence as producers of woods of
the hardest and finest texture for cabinet purposes—granted further that the other new trees
have the capacity for growth which the hybrid
walnuts show—and a triumvirate of trees would
be attained that could be depended on to go
forth and gladden the devastated hillsides and
valleys with trees that would jointly meet
every need of carpenter and cabinetmaker,
adding incalculable billions to the wealth of
our nation.

And of course we need not by any means con-
fine attention to these few most typical trees.
There are beeches and chestnuts that are near
relatives of the oak, each of which serves its own
particular purpose as the provider of wood having unique quality. The beech and birch, for
example, are prized by the chairmaker for his
furniture, and for the making of carpenter tools

and such like instruments. The chestnut makes railroad ties that are thought to have no equal and telegraph poles of requisite strength and straightness.

Then there are other families that have their valued representatives. The hickories have already been referred to. The maples must not be overlooked, as they furnish highly prized woods to the cabinetmaker. The tulip tree supplies a light-colored wood used by cabinetmaker and coach builder. The basswood or linden gives a wood of peculiar fiber that meets the needs of carvers and instrument makers. The willows and their allies; various members of the birch family; the buttonwood tree or sycamore; and the locusts and their allies are other native trees that are of value as they stand and are well worth developing.

The plant experimenter who works with these different trees, being guided by their botanical affinities, but making careful tests even where he doubts the possibility of hybridization, will be almost certain to have his efforts rewarded by the production of some trees of new varieties that will not only duplicate the unexpected qualities of the hybrid walnuts, but will doubtless also reveal unpredicted traits that will give them added value.

Patience will be required in carrying out the work, for the tree is long-lived and experiments in its development are quite different from those in the development of annual plants. Yet something of the probable results of an experiment can be judged even from observation of seedlings in their first year. And by hurrying the hybrid plants by the method of grafting, it will be possible greatly to shorten the generations.

Still, it is not to be denied that the work of developing new races of trees is one that should preferably command the attention of the younger generation. In particular, it should be carried on under government supervision, as part of the great work of reforestation, the necessity for which has only in recent years been clearly realized by those in authority or by the community in general.

Messages from the Past

The oft-cited hybrid walnuts supply us with tangible evidence of the possibility of developing new races of trees having much-to-be-desired qualities of rapid growth, through hybridization of the existing species.

Such evidence as has been suggested is more forceful and convincing than any amount of theoretical argument. But it may be of interest to support this evidence, and in doing so to reveal additional reasons for belief that the same principles will apply to other forest trees, by recalling briefly the story of the vicissitudes through which the existing trees have passed and through which the diversified hereditary factors were implanted in their racial heredity.

A knowledge of this story we owe to the geological botanists. They have sought diligently in the rocks for fossil remains, and by joint effort, searching all around the world, have been able to reproduce a picture of the main story of the evolution of existing forms of vegetable life.

It is by recalling the story which they tell us, and thus alone, that we are enabled somewhat clearly to apprehend the possibilities of variation, and through variation of so-called new development—consisting essentially of the recombination and intensification of old ancestral traits—that we have witnessed in the case of many tribes of plants in the course of our experiments.

A brief resume of this story of plant life in the past, with particular reference to our own flora, will serve in the present connection to explain why there is every warrant for believing that each and every one of our forest trees contains submerged in its heredity the potentialities of a

OLIVE TREES

Until somewhat recently the olive has been grown chiefly in the region of the Mediterranean. Of late years, however, it has become a very important commercial crop in California, and the California olives have become famous everywhere for their size and good qualities in general. The picture shows a typical hillside olive orchard near Santa Rosa.

development of which its exterior appearance gives but faint suggestion.

It appears that there is full warrant for the belief that the modern flora originated in the Northern Hemisphere, and probably in the region of the North Pole. During the so-called Mesozoic Age, the conditions of the Northern Hemisphere were those that would nowadays be described as tropical or subtropical. There were palms growing in Europe and in Alaska, and such species as the sequoia, the plane trees, maples, and magnolias grew even at a relatively late period as far north as the seventieth degree of latitude. Remains of conifers have been found within nine degrees of the pole itself; remains of palms in Alaska coal measures, and of the sassafras along the western coast.

At this early period the flora of the entire Northern Hemisphere was, as regards its trees, essentially comparable to the existing flora of America to-day.

There were oaks and beeches scarcely distinguishable from existing species.

There were birches and planes and willows closely related to the living species known as *Salix candida*.

There were laurels not unlike their modern representatives, the sassafras and cinnamon tree, and myrtles and ivies that are represented by existing descendants of allied forms.

And there were magnolias and tulip trees of which the existing tulip tree of the United States is an obviously direct and not very greatly modified descendant.

All these trees grew far to the north, and luxuriated, as has been said, in a temperature that we of to-day would call subtropical, for in that day it is probable that the North Pole was tilted far toward the sun, and that the conditions that we now think of as tropical existed only in the region of the pole itself.

Then there came the slow progressive period of refrigeration. The tropical climate of the pole was succeeded by an age of ice, and the successive ice sheets slowly pressed southward, driving the plants no less than the animals before them along all parallels of longitude, until the flowers and faunas that intermingled in the arctic region were scattered along diverging paths to people the continents separated by the wide stretches of the Atlantic and the Pacific oceans.

It may seem strange to speak of plants fleeing before the ice sheet. But it must be understood that the plant is a migratory being, when considered as a race, notwithstanding the stationary habit of the individual. Plants put forth mobile seeds, and devise many strange ways of insuring their wide dissemination. They are always seeking new territories, and, granted proper conditions, always finding them.

And it is only such plants as could migrate with relative celerity that were able to maintain existence and escape extermination by fleeing southward when the era of cold succeeded to the warm era in the arctic regions and when the arctic chill gradually spread southward and encompassed all the higher and middle latitudes of the Northern Hemisphere.

The plants that chanced to flee southward along the land surface that we now term Europe found their further flight checked when they reached the stretches of mountains extending east and west that we now term the Alps. Here thousands of species made a last stand and ultimately perished.

But the plants that were fortunate enough to choose the other avenues of escape, passing down across the land surfaces that we now term America and Asia, were not obstructed in their flight. The long ranges of the Appalachians and Rockies and Sierras in particular served, as it were, to guide the line of march and aid the flight.

So the American species made their way to the region of the Gulf, and some of them even to the southern continent. And when the ice sheet finally receded, they were able to make their way northward again, though never to their former habitat; whereas Europe was treeless until the plant life of Asia spread westward to repeople it.

Such is the explanation that the paleobotanist gives us of the fact that the indigenous vegetation of America to-day is closely similar to that which stocked the subarctic regions of the entire Northern Hemisphere in the geological period known as the Mesozoic—a period that seems infinitely remote when measured in terms of human history, yet which in the scale of time as measured by the geologist is relatively recent.

Such trees as the sequoia, we are told, are survivors of that ancient régime that chanced to find hospitable shelter on the western slopes of the Sierras. Similarly the tulip tree of the east, with the blossoms that seem anomalous for a tree, should be regarded as the souvenir of a past age —a lone representative of vast tribes that once flourished in tropical luxuriance in regions that now give scant support to moss and lichen and stunted conifers.

All in all, we are told, the remaining vegetation of to-day, varied though it seems, is but a scant reminiscence of that of the period preceding the ice ages. Only a few species, relatively speaking, were able to make their migration rapidly enough to escape destruction. These included a certain number, like the sequoia and the tulip tree, that were able to reach coigns of vantage that permitted them to exist without changing essentially from their sun-loving habit. But in the main the tribes that escaped destruction were those that were more plastic and developed a hardiness that enabled them to withstand extremes of temperature not far beyond the limits of the ice sheet. Others made their way northward again when the ice sheet receded.

And as the climate of ensuing ages, after the successive periods of intense refrigeration, everywhere retained, throughout the central and eastern portions of America, curious reminiscences of both the tropical and the arctic, the plants that finally repopulated the devastated territories were those that had learned, through the strange vicissitudes of their ancestors, to thrive where the thermometer in summer might rise to the one hundred degree mark, and where in winter the mercury might freeze.

Such are the conditions under which pines and oaks and willows and beeches and black walnuts and allied trees exist to-day in the regions of northern America where they flourish.

They can withstand the glare of a tropical sun in summer because their ancestors reveled in a tropical climate. And they can withstand equally the arctic cold of winter because their ancestors of other ages were forced to subsist under arctic conditions.

The versatile trees that, thanks to the racial recollection of these vicissitudes, can adapt themselves to the inhospitable conditions of our modern climate are but dwarfed representatives of ancient races of giants. To preserve life at all it was necessary for them to conserve their energies; and gigantic growth is feasible only for plants that can send their roots into rich, well-watered soils and can likewise draw sustenance perennially from the atmosphere, unhampered by long periods of dormancy when life itself is threatened.

But these dwarfed races carry in their germ plasm, submerged but not eliminated, factors for giant growth; factors for such development as would adapt them to life in the tropics; factors also for such development as would adapt them for life in the arctics.

Their hereditary factors, in a word, are as varied as have been their past environments. So, what each tree is now exteriorly gives us but faint suggestion of what it might be were its unrealized hereditary possibilities to be made actualities.

So far as we know at present, the only way in which these unrealized possibilities may in any conspicuous measure be brought out is by hybridizing species that have so far diverged that they lie almost at the limits of affinity. By such union of hereditary tendencies that have long been disunited, racial traits that are reminiscent of the old days when the Northern Hemisphere enjoyed a tropical climate may be revived, and a tendency to repeat a gigantic growth that characterizes ancestors vastly remote will be revealed.

Such is the explanation of the strange and otherwise inexplicable phenomena of gigantism manifested by my hybrid walnuts. And such is our warrant for believing that all other species of native trees have possibilities of development that are unrevealed in the exterior appearance of their present-day representatives and that can be revealed, so far as we know, only by hybridization.

TREES WHOSE PRODUCTS ARE USEFUL SUBSTANCES

Sugar Maples and Other Trees

EVERYONE who had the good fortune to be born in New England and to live in the country will treasure among the most pleasant reminiscences of his boyhood the recollection of his first visit to a "sugar bush."

The sweet sap drawn through a magic spigot from a hole in the tree trunk; the boiling kettle in which the sap was transformed into the most delectable of syrups; the transformation of the syrup into a wax of quite matchless flavor by pouring it on the snow—these are things that have no counterpart. They must be experienced to be appreciated, and no one who has experienced them is likely to forget them.

To those who have not been privileged to visit a sugar bush, the product of the maple is usually known only in its ultimate crystallized form in which it constitutes a brownish sugar of characteristic and delectable flavor. And I regret to

say that many people who suppose themselves
familiar with this product know it only in
a diluted and adulterated form in which
only a suggestion remains of the real maple
quality.

Nor does there seem to be much prospect of
improvement in this regard, for the maple tree
is seldom or never cultivated for the garnering
of its unique crop. The relatively small quantity
of maple sugar that finds its way to the market
is the product of trees that chanced to grow in
the woodland and they are reserved not so much
as sugar producers but as ultimate material for
lumber. Yet maple sugar is a sweet of acknowledged quality, and one that deserves a larger
measure of recognition as a commercial product
than has hitherto been given it.

Possibly the time may come when maple trees
will be cultivated for the production of sugar.
But it is hardly likely that such cultivation of
the maple can ever constitute a significant industry, because the product of a single tree is
relatively insignificant.

It is only the fact that the sugar maple has
wood of such quality of fiber as to make it valuable for the cabinetmaker that could justify
the cultivation of these trees as a commercial
enterprise.

On the other hand, the amateur orchardist might do far worse than to set a row of "sugar" maples, as ornamental trees about the borders of his orchard or gardens, regarding the capacity of the tree to produce a certain amount of sugar as an incidental attraction that adds to the value of a tree that otherwise is deserving because of its beauty of form and general attractiveness.

The production of the sweet sap that has made the sugar maple famous gives this particular species exceptional interest among the members of a very meritorious family. Just why this species should have developed the capacity to produce so sugary a sap in such abundance, it would perhaps be difficult to say. A certain amount of sap may be drawn from the tissues of other maples, and even from the walnut and butternut, and in diluted form from the birches; but only the sugar maple produces sap of such quality as to be of real value.

WHEN THE SAP RUNS BEST

And of course it is well known that the sugar maple itself has a "flow" of sap that is worth tapping, for a very brief period each season, just as winter is merging into spring. It is traditional at least among the makers of maple sugar that the sap runs best in those days of early spring when the sun shines brightly while there is a cover of snow on the ground. At this time, all that is necessary is to bore an auger hole in the trunk of the tree, and insert a spigot or grooved stick to guide the sap into the bucket.

A single tree may be tapped in several places, and a bucket of sap will run from each spigot in the course of a day.

The sap itself is a clear, watery fluid, the sweet taste of which gives assurance of the quality of sugar it contains. By boiling the sap to evaporate the surplus water, a thick sirup is produced which crystallizes on cooling, producing the maple sugar of commerce.

Nothing is added to the sap and nothing but part of its watery content is taken away from it—that is to say, if it is honestly made. The sugar as the maple supplies it, is a perfect product requiring no dilution and calling for no elaborate process of manufacture.

Perhaps it is not so much matter for surprise that maple trees produce this sweet sap in such abundance as that other trees do not more generally imitate its example. For the function of the sugar in supplying nourishment for the young buds before the leaves are sufficiently expanded to begin their work of sugar manufacture is clearly enough understood. All other deciduous trees must supply nutriment in similar way to their growing buds.

But in the case of other trees, either the sap will not flow in abundance or it is of such quality as to have no value.

The manner of production of the sap may be more or less accurately inferred from what we have already learned of plant physiology. We know that the leaves of the tree metamorphose water and carbon into sugary substances which in turn are transferred to various parts of the plant to be stored, usually in the form of starch. In the case of the maple, we may assume that the carbohydrates, as they are manufactured in the leaf laboratories, are transferred in the current of sap that flows downward from the leaves through branches and trunk as a countercurrent in the cambium until it finally finds its way to the roots of the tree and is there stored for the winter.

When spring comes and it is time for the new leaf buds to put forth, the supplies of nourishment are retransformed into soluble sugars, dissolved in the water that is taken in by the rootlets, and transferred from cell to cell and along the little canals in the wood under the cambium layer of the bark, until they reach the twigs

THE CALIFORNIA CHINQUA-
PIN AS AN ORNAMEN-
TAL TREE

This beautiful specimen of the wild California chinquapin grows on our grounds at Sebastopol. The California chinquapin tree has obvious merits of its own as an ornamental shrub, as this picture clearly testifies. It is evergreen, with foliage of golden color underneath, and is appropriately named Castanea chrysophylla.

where the leaf buds they are to nourish are located.

It is doubtless the so-called "root pressure" (which we have been led to interpret as due to osmosis) forcing the sap upward that causes it to flow from the wound in the tree made by the auger. To what extent the interference with the supply of nourishment that was being convoyed to the buds retards their development, might be interesting matter for observation.

But this is something that does not greatly concern the sugar maker, and to which he doubtless never gives a thought.

It is also interesting to conjecture whether it might be possible by selective breeding to produce a variety of sugar maple that will furnish sap in exceptional quantity and of unusual quality. The case is obviously different from that of the sugar prune or the sugar beet, both of which have been trained to increase their sugar content.

But there is no doubt that different individual sugar maples differ widely in their sap producing, or at least in their sap rendering, quality. Presumably the difference may be due to the size of the root system. But so far as I know there are no accurate observations on the subject, nor has anything been done to determine whether a better race of sugar maples could be developed.

OTHER PLANT JUICES

The extraordinary plant laboratories that manufacture sugars out of water and air are capable of transforming these sugars into many unusual substances, differing in character with the constitution of the particular plant.

There are certain classes of juicy exudates, however, which appear to have characteristics that make them useful to plants of many types. Prominent among these are the milky juices that when dried constitute rubber, and the resinous ones that constitute tars and resins and turpentine.

Nothing could be physically much more dissimilar than a piece of rubber and a teaspoonful of oil of turpentine.

But the chemist tells us that each of these substances is composed exclusively of the two elements carbon and hydrogen; the only difference being that the turpentine molecule has ten atoms of carbon and sixteen of hydrogen, whereas the molecule of rubber has eight carbon atoms and seven atoms of hydrogen.

Just how the elements are compounded, and just why they should make up substances of such unique characteristics when brought together in these particular proportions, even the chemist does not know. Nor, until recently, was he able to duplicate the feat of building up these complex molecules, even though he is perfectly familiar with the general properties of the atoms of both carbon and hydrogen.

In very recent years, however, chemists have been at work on the problem of compounding the atoms in such a way as to get them together in the right combination to produce organic substances. And, although this work is only at its beginning, a good measure of success has been attained.

In particular, the chemists of Germany and England have recently succeeded in combining carbon and hydrogen in the proportion of eight atoms of the former to seven of the latter and thus have produced an artificial rubber that is not merely an imitation rubber but is as truly pure rubber as if it had been produced in the cellular system of a plant.

The artificial product may be said to be somewhat more pure than the natural, inasmuch as the latter is more or less contaminated by extraneous products.

Reference has elsewhere been made to the familiar feat of the chemist through which the famous dyestuffs, indigo and madder, have been manufactured in the laboratory, and manufac-

tured so cheaply as to compete successfully with
the natural product of the indigo and madder
plants. What was a large plant industry only a
few years ago has thus ceased to have importance. The indigo plant is still cultivated in the
east, but the entire industry has been changed by
the discoveries of the chemist.

Only a few years ago a plant known as the
tarweed (*Madia*), to which we have had occasion to refer in another connection, was gathered
and its juices extracted for the making of madder. But it would not pay to undertake this
work now, since the chemist has learned how to
make madder from coal tar and hence has sub-
stituted for a plant industry an enterprise associated with the manufacture of gas.

It will doubtless be a long time before the manufacture of artificial rubber makes corresponding encroachments on the industry of manufacturing rubber from the plant juices. Still
it is quite within the possibilities that this
may come to pass in the course of the coming
generation.

In the meantime, the rubber industry is a great
and important one, and the principal trees that
supply the juices that on evaporating constitute
rubber are cultivated in vast plantations in various tropical regions. Moreover rubber is gath-

ered from wild trees of several species, although in recent years the cultivated trees have largely been depended upon to meet the growing needs of the industry.

Trees of the genus *Hevea* are the most important source of rubber. But there are many other trees, the juices of which contain the essential constituents of rubber in the right combination, and many of these have commercial possibilities.

I have referred in another connection to my experiments with tropical plants of the genus *Asclepias,* relatives of the familiar milkweed.

Tentative experiments have been undertaken to discover whether these plants might be developed to a stage that would make them commercially valuable as producers of rubber. The recent discoveries of the chemist make experiments in this line somewhat less valuable than they hitherto seemed. Yet the demand for rubber is so great, in these days of electricity and automobiles, that there seems just now little danger of overstocking the market. And if a plant could be developed that could be grown in temperate regions, and that would produce the rubber-forming juices in adequate quantity, such a plant would constitute a very valuable acquisition for a long time to come, even should natural rubber ultimately be supplanted by the laboratory product.

The method of gathering the so-called latex or milky juice, which is virtually rubber in solution, is curiously similar to the method of obtaining the sap of the sugar maple. Indeed the latex may be drawn in precisely the same way, by boring a hole in the trunk of the rubber tree and inserting a grooved stick along which the juice will run into a receptacle. But the cultivators are not usually content with so slow a method, and there are various methods of tapping the tree that expose a larger surface of the cambium layer and thus extract the milky juices in larger quantity.

In the case of the wild trees it is not unusual for the natives of Mexico, Central America, and South America to make a series of V-shaped incisions in the bark of the tree, placing a receptacle at the point of each "V" and thus securing a relatively enormous amount of fluid regardless of the fact that they jeopardize the life of the tree itself.

Of course cultivated groves or plantations are tapped in a more conservative way, but the principle involved is everywhere the same.

The latex of the rubber tree is comparable to the sugary sap of the maple. It appears to be a mere accident that this juice has the property of coagulating to form the substance called rubber which we now find so important. But this substance, obviously, as man uses it, has small place in the economy of the plant. Coagulated latex would serve no better purpose in the tissues of the rubber tree than would coagulated blood in the veins of a human being.

OILS AND RESINS

Of course the latex of the rubber tree might exude when the tree received an accidental injury, as from a falling limb, and in such case it would be advantageous to the tree to have the juice coagulate, just as coagulated blood is useful to a wounded man. In each case coagulation prevents excessive hemorrhage.

Possibly this may explain the quality of the latex, its capacity to coagulate having been developed through natural selection. But under normal conditions, at least, the latex is always fluid, and its properties are little more like those of rubber than are the properties of the maple tree like those of sugar.

Of course the same thing is true of the plant juices that when dried or partially evaporated constitute the various gums and resins. As manufactured in the tree they are transformed

THE VARIEGATED BOX ELDER

Although popularly known everywhere as an elder, this is really a maple, listed by the botanist as the ash-leaved maple (Acer negundo). It is a hardy tree of rapid growth, much prized for planting in semiarid regions. There are several varieties, giving opportunity for experiments in selective breeding.

sugar products, and they are always in solution. Only when the juices are exposed to the air, as when they exude from an injured surface, do they coagulate to form the gummy or resinous substances that become articles of commerce.

In some cases the exudate may be separated into two or more commercial constituents. Such is the case with the juice of those trees that produce turpentine. The liquid that flows from the tree, corresponding to the sap of the maple and the latex of the rubber tree, may be evaporated or distilled in such a way as to be changed in part to a solid gummy or even vitreous substance, and in part to the somewhat volatile fluid familiar as turpentine.

Turpentine, unlike rubber, was known to the ancients, and was an extensive article of commerce in classical times. The original tree from which it was obtained is known as the terebinth tree. It is a native of the islands and shores of the Mediterranean and western Asia.

There are many trees, however, the sap of which has this resinous property, including most members of the family of conifers. The principal supply of common turpentine, in Europe, is obtained from the so-called sea pine, grown largely in France. The Scotch fir, the Norway pine, and the Corsican pine are other sources.

In the United States the swamp pine and the so-called loblolly trees that grow in the swamps of North and South Carolina and Georgia, are the chief source of the commercial turpentines, although various other species are more or less utilized.

A gum of peculiar quality that is highly prized for some industrial purposes is obtained from the balsam fir (*Abies balsamea*), and is known as Canada balsam.

Hitherto, the producers of turpentine have been found in the wild state, and no one, probably, has given a thought to the possibility of developing races of pines that produce an exceptional quantity of the resin and turpentine-forming juices. But with the modern tendency to apply scientific methods to forestation in general, doubtless the question will ultimately arise as to whether the turpentine trees may not be improved along with the timber producers.

That trees of the same species differ quite radically in the amount of the valuable juices is certain, so there would appear to be no reason why it may not be possible to develop varieties of trees that will be conspicuous for this quality, just as other trees have been improved as to their powers of growth or their capacity to produce abundant crops of fruit.

Varied Products of the Plant Laboratory

An incidental use of the resinous exudate of various trees is the production of chewing gum.

The habit of gum chewing appears to have originated or at least to have gained chief popularity in America in comparatively recent times. The resin that exudes from the spruce was the substance that was chiefly used, under the name of spruce gum, until somewhat recently. But of late years the chewing gum industry has reached proportions that make it impossible to meet the demand from this source. And it has been found that ordinary resin, combined with sugar and linseed oil, with some flavoring added, serves the purpose of the original spruce gum so the latter is now seldom seen in the market. More recently chicle, a gummy substance which exudes from several tropical trees, has been imported in great quantities, and is now supplanting all other sources of gum.

The supplying of turpentine and its products gives the conifers high rank among trees that produce commercial by-products of great importance. But with the exception of the pines, the trees that produce really important exudates or oils or chemicals are indigenous to the tropics,

or at least are confined to the warm temperate
zone. I have thought many times in recent years
that I should like to have a plant laboratory in
the tropics for testing tropical plants as to production of useful commercial products, and for
development of improved varieties of plants the
products of which are already utilized.

It would be worth while, for example, to make
very extensive experiments by way of testing
the qualities of the different trees that deposit
in their bark the bitter compounds known as
alkaloids, a galaxy of which are prized for their
medicinal properties. These are very complex
combinations of carbon, hydrogen, oxygen, and
nitrogen. That is to say, they have the same constituents as protoplasm itself and differ from the
gum and resins that we have just been considering in that each molecule contains at least one
atom of nitrogen.

The sugars, it will be recalled, occupy an intermediate place, inasmuch as they, unlike the
resins and rubber, contain oxygen; but they contain no nitrogen. The formulæ given by the
chemist for the different alkaloids are intricate
but they differ from one another only in the matter of a few more or a few less atoms of one or
another of the four constituents of which they are
all made up.

There is, for example, only the difference of one atom of carbon and of four atoms of hydrogen between a molecule of quinine and a molecule of strychnine. Considering that the molecules comprise in the aggregate not far from fifty atoms, in each case, this discrepancy seems trifling. That the two drugs should have such utterly different effects upon the human system is a mystery that will be solved only when a much fuller knowledge is gained as to the physiological processes than anyone has at present.

But the plant developer, of course, has no concern with this aspect of the subject. What interests him is the knowledge that different races of cinchona trees, for example, are known to vary greatly as to the proportion of commercial alkaloid deposited in their bark. And the same is true of most or all other producers of commercial alkaloids.

Apparently there is a splendid field, then, for the plant experimenter, could he establish a laboratory and experiment garden in the tropics, in the development of improved races of cinchona and almost innumerable other suppliers of medicinal alkaloids. The monetary return from such an enterprise would probably be larger than that which usually rewards the efforts of the plant developer in temperate zones, because the field is

AN ACACIA TREE IN BLOOM

There are more than a hundred species of acacias introduced into California from the Southern Hemisphere, and many of them have become very popular. Their value as ornamental trees is well suggested by this photograph. Unfortunately, they are not as hardy as could be desired, although they thrive almost everywhere in California. One of the African species of acacia yields the gum arabic of commerce.

virgin, and because there is no present possibility
of competition outside the tropics.

It remains to be said that there are a few other
trees and shrubs of our own latitude that may
advantageously command the attention of the
plant developer for the improvement of quantity
or quality of their products.

It seems not unlikely that the horse chestnut,
or buckeye, could be so educated as to become a
profitable starch producer. At present this tree
produces an abundant crop of nuts, but these are
worthless because they contain a bitter principle
that makes them inedible. Yet the nut of the
buckeye is very starchy and if the bitter principle
could be eliminated without too much expense
there is no reason why it should not prove both
wholesome and nutritious. The Indians grind
the nuts to make meal. When this is soaked
in water the poisonous principle is partially removed, and the residue is cooked and eaten.

I have experimented somewhat in testing the
tremendously productive western buckeye as to
its possibilities of improvement. As long ago as
1877 I began work on this tree, and continued
the experiments in a small way for a number of
years. It was observed that there was great
variation as to productiveness of trees, as to size
of nuts, and also as to bitterness of the nuts them-

selves, and I am convinced that it would be possible to develop a variety in which the bitter principle would be greatly reduced in amount and perhaps altogether eliminated, and that at the same time a nut having an even higher starch content could be developed.

It has been found possible with the South American plant called the cassava to utilize roots that contain a poisonous principle for the production of so important a commercial product as tapioca. It is not unlikely that the nuts of the horse chestnut, if developed until it had a still higher starch content, could be utilized in somewhat the same way, even though the bitter principle was not entirely eliminated.

There are some members of the laurel family, also, that produce commercial products that make them worthy of attention. The camphor tree is too tender to be grown in the northern latitudes, but its relative, the sassafras, is a common tree throughout the Eastern States, thriving even in New York and New England. Its bark furnishes the characteristic flavoring that is used for perfuming soaps and for similar purposes. The production of the sassafras would not constitute a significant industry under any circumstances, doubtless, yet there would be a measure of scientific interest in testing its capacities for improvement, and not unlikely new uses would be found if it were available in larger quantity.

Another tribe that furnishes a product of a unique quality is that represented by a familiar wild shrub known in the Eastern States as the waxberry or candleberry (*Myrica carolinensis*) and sometimes also spoken of as the bayberry owing to the fragrance of its leaves.

This shrub bears an abundance of small berries from which may be extracted a quantity of hard greenish fragrant wax, which was formerly much prized for the making of candles, and which has a value for the other uses to which wax is put.

Many years ago, while traveling in the East, I found a candleberry bush that was of compact growth and that produced an unusually large crop of waxy berries. Seed was collected and brought to California, and for several years it was worked upon, until by selection a variety was developed that produced at least ten times as many berries and ten times as much wax as the average wild plant. At the same time I experimented with a Japanese member of the genus known as *M. rubra,* and also with the California species, *M. californica,* which is a tree growing forty to fifty feet in height.

The endeavor was made to cross the three Myricas in the hope of producing new varieties

of value, but did not succeed, no doubt because
the attempt was not carried out with sufficient
pertinacity. The California species produces a
wax of much darker color than the eastern one,
but of about the same degree of hardness. I
still have several fine blocks of wax that were
produced from these shrubs and trees during the
time of the experiment. Although not successful in combining the different candleberry
shrubs, the experiments were carried far enough
to show the possibility of great improvement by
mere selection. If there were a market for the
wax, the plant might be well worth improving.
These plants were finally destroyed to make
room for other shrubs. This is another case in
which a product of intrinsic value has failed to
find a market, largely, no doubt, because the
plant that produces it has hitherto not been
brought under cultivation, and hence has not
produced a sufficient crop to bring it to the attention of the public and to create a market.

It would not be surprising, however, if the
candleberry should be thought valuable enough
in future for development and cultivation on an
extensive scale. For the wax that it produces
is of unique quality, and it is almost certain
to be found of value in connection with some
commercial industry.

TREES AND SHRUBS FOR SHADE AND ORNAMENT

SOME MISCELLANEOUS TREE EXPERIMENTS

DOUBTLESS the most interesting tree in the world is the *Sequoia*. The mere fact that this is the most gigantic of all existing trees gives it distinction. But it has added interest because it represents a link with the remote past.

Of course it might be said that any existing vegetable represents a link with the past, since every race has its lines of ancestry tracing back to primordial times. But the Sequoias represent the past in a somewhat different sense, inasmuch as it has maintained more fixedly the traits of its remote ancestors than has been done by any other tree, probably, that now grows in the Northern Hemisphere, with the possible exception of the tulip tree, which represents a quite different type of vegetation.

The story of the Sequoia's fight for life during the remote geological ages when the climate of

149

the Northern Hemisphere was changing, has been outlined in an earlier chapter. Could we know the details of the story, we should doubtless find that the ancestors of the *Sequoia* migrated southward before the chilling blasts of successive glacial epochs, and made their way northward again in the intervening periods. And of course the present age may represent merely another of these interglacial epochs, during which the *Sequoia* has carried its return march along the coast to about the fortieth parallel of latitude. It maintains in this location its proud position as the one champion of the ancient traditions. And perhaps it will still maintain them in some remote epoch of the future when another ice age has driven man from the Northern Hemisphere and reduced the civilization of the twentieth century to a half-forgotten tradition.

Be that as it may, the Sequoias stand to-day as sister giants in an age of pygmies. Individual trees that are still young according to the reckoning of their tribe were gigantic trees when Columbus discovered America.

And Sequoias that are moderately old have witnessed the ceaseless change of the seasons since the period, perhaps, when Moor and Christian were battling for supremacy in Europe in the dark age that preceded the segregation of the

modern nations of Europe. The patriarchs of
the race were living in the days that saw the
building of the Egyptian pyramids and many
of these now in the prime of life and vigor were
growing when Moses walked the earth.

A tree with such racial traditions and with
such individual representatives is surely entitled
to be considered the most interesting tree in the
world.

Whoever has camped in a primeval forest of
Sequoias will attest that merely to enter into the
presence of these colossal antediluvians is to
experience an almost overwhelming sense of
their grandeur. And it is the common experience
that this feeling of awe grows day by day and
becomes overpowering if you linger like a lost
pygmy in the shadows of the giants.

From our present standpoint the interest in
the Sequoias hinges on the possibility of growing
seedlings or transplanting saplings for ornamental purposes in the parks and fields. It is
rather strange that the attempt to do this has
not been carried out more extensively. Curiously
enough, the redwoods are grown more in England than they are anywhere in America outside
the regions where they are indigenous. But
doubtless the climatic conditions account for this.
The trees thrive fairly well in the relatively mild

A YOUNG SEQUOIA GIGANTEA

This beautiful evergreen tree is a young Sequoia about six years old, growing on my home place. Note the compact growth of branches from the very ground. Contrast this young tree with the old Sequoia shown in the next picture.

climate of England, but they find the winters of the north-central and the northeastern United States prohibitive.

A tree that has weathered successive ice ages should not mind the winters of the present era, even at the northern boundaries of the United States, one might suppose. But such an inference misses the chief point of the Sequoia's ancestral story. In fact, the giant trees are alive to-day in something like their pristine form because they migrated before the ice sheets and finally found a place of refuge west of the Sierras where they were sheltered from the northern blasts and given protection by the tempered breezes of the Pacific. As compared with the other conifers—pines, spruces, hemlocks, cedars, and the rest—the Sequoias are really tender trees. They are hardy indeed in contrast with their ancestors of still remoter geological times. But they have never developed that extreme hardiness that characterizes their modified and stunted cousins.

Nevertheless it has been found possible to raise the *Sequoia gigantea* as far north as central New York. But the tree does not really thrive in regions so inhospitable, and the redwood is even more tender. In central and south-central regions of the United States, however, the giant trees can be grown to better advantage, and here they should find a place as ornamental trees that has not hitherto been accorded them.

In the region of Washington, D. C., the *Sequoia* has proved altogether hardy, and of course it may be grown readily anywhere along the Atlantic Coast south of this region. It is a tree of extremely rapid growth, almost equaling the eucalyptus. The redwood also is of such rapid growth under cultivation that it soon overshadows most other trees. Indeed, it grows so rapidly and requires so much room that it is hardly adapted to use as an ornamental tree except in very large grounds.

I have raised the giant *Sequoia* (it is known technically as *Sequoia gigantea*) in the nursery from seed, and the redwood (*Sequoia sempervirens*) from cuttings as well as from seed. The cuttings do fairly well if started in the fall and treated like cuttings of other conifers.

As to the matter of selection and development, the redwood itself may probably be regarded as a comparatively recent variation from the form of the giant *Sequoia*. The ancestors of the redwood took up their location in the valleys nearer the ocean and were modified until they are considered to rank as a distinct species. But the similarity of the two forms is obvious, and the two species stand in a class by themselves—obviously allied to other conifers in the form of leaf and cone and manner of growth, yet so far outranking all others as to be properly thought of as representatives of a unique order of vegetation.

Whether further modifications in the giant trees could be wrought by hybridizing the two forms or by selection among variant seedlings is a question of interest.

Presumably, such modifications could be brought about were there time for it. But in dealing with a tree that is a mere child when it has outlived half a dozen generations of men, the plant developer feels himself in the presence of forces that lie almost beyond his ken.

Moreover the attempt to deal experimentally with the redwood is made difficult by the fact that the tree seldom bears seed. Some of the woodmen claim that it bears once in seven years, but this is doubtless a mere guess, instigated by the popular superstition connected with the number seven. On one occasion, some thirty-five years ago, I was informed that the redwoods were loaded with seed, and went out with some helpers and gathered a dozen grain sacks or more of the cones, which could be obtained in any desired quantity. On drying the cones I found that the seeds themselves made up half the total weight.

There was a wide variation in the cones themselves and in the seed from different trees.

The seed when dried kept its germinating quality for seven or eight years. But only a very small proportion of the seeds will germinate under any circumstances, even when fresh. This seems to be especially true of seeds collected from the younger trees—a fact that accentuates the already sufficient difficulties that confront the plant developer who cares to undertake the rather discouraging task of experimental breeding with these antique giants.

Nevertheless, it should be recorded that a certain amount of work has been done with the redwood, particularly in the way of selecting trees that bear weeping branches and other unique characters. I have observed that seedlings usually show the characteristic drooping branches of the parent form. Most of the seedlings show a rather wide range of variation of foliage, particularly where seed from different localities is sown. Some are much lighter in color than others, and there are various interesting characteristics that may be noted by a close observer, leaving no doubt that there is sufficient material for the purposes of the plant developer.

Doubtless anyone who has patience to undertake the task will be able to produce various types of redwoods that will reveal interesting characteristics of the remote racial strains that now are so blended in the existing representatives of the family as to be scarcely observable.

It is not best to attempt to speak except in a general way of the other members of the great tribe of conifers, the merits of most of which, as ornamental trees, are familiar to every garden and landscape architect.

There are some scores of genera and some hundreds of species of conifers, but the varieties are too numerous and too intricately blended for accurate computation.

No other single region has so many forms of evergreens, and ones that show such wide range of variation, as the Pacific Coast region. It has been estimated that there are as many species of conifers in California as in all the rest of the world.

But the conifers of one kind and another grow everywhere throughout the colder regions of the Northern Hemisphere, some of them making their way also to parts of the South.

Every one of them is an object lesson in the possibility of plant variation; for as a class they represent a modification of leaf form of the most

THE LARGEST TREE IN THE WORLD

This giant Sequoia, growing in the Mariposa Grove, in the Yosemite National Park, is known as the "Grizzly Giant." It is 34 feet in diameter and 225 feet high. It is estimated to contain more than one million feet of lumber. The first limb is 100 feet from the ground, and six feet in diameter. Doubtless the tree originally had limbs all the way from the ground, but the lower ones have died in the course of the ages that mark the life of this extraordinary tree.

striking character to meet the exigencies of a changing environment.

Time was, doubtless, when the ancestors of the conifers had flat, spreading leaves like the leaves of other forms of vegetation. But when the climatic conditions changed, the pampering influences of warmth and moisture being supplanted by the chill and drought that presaged the onset of perpetual winter, a premium was put on the conservation of plant energies. Whereas before the elements favored the tree that could raise its head highest and thrust out the most luxuriant growth of spreading leaves to absorb the carbon from the heavily laden atmosphere, the time now came when the tree that had a smaller system of branches to nourish and a less expansive leaf system had better chance of maintaining existence.

So in the lapse of ages, the conditions becoming more and more hard, the trees that varied in the direction of smaller size and narrower leaves had an ever-increasing advantage. These survived where their more rank-growing and luxuriant-leafed fellows perished.

Thus generation after generation natural selection operated to modify the size of the trees and to develop a race of trees with narrow leaves, which ultimately were reduced to the form of needles.

Such leaves, offering the largest possible surface in proportion to their bulk, could gain nourishment from an impoverished atmosphere, and at the same time would obstruct the rays of the sun but little, so that the entire foliage of the tree might secure a share of the all-essential light which now, age on age, became less and less bright as the earth may have changed the direction of its axis.

Of course there were other trees that did not undergo this modification. But these were forced either to make more rapid migrations to the south or to give up the fight altogether and to submit to extermination. The only evergreen trees that were able to maintain existence in the regions where the climate became exceedingly cold were those that had developed the new type of leaf form, and had learned to conserve their energies to the last degree.

But of course the trees that took on this new habit varied among themselves, and as they spread to different regions such variations were developed and fixed under the influence of different environments, until many tribes of needle-leafed trees were developed so differently as to constitute the races that the modern botanist terms pine and spruce and cypress and juniper and hemlock and yew and cedar, etc.

Representatives of all the chief genera of conifers have a recognized place among ornamental trees and are everywhere popular in cold climates. The variations among the different species are so obvious as to attract the attention of the least observant. And the opportunity to develop any fixed new form is correspondingly good.

I have raised large numbers of conifers of many species, and have experimented with them in the way of selection, producing in some cases varieties of considerable interest; for example, several beautiful varieties of the various *Abies,* including some very conspicuous forms with weeping foliage; also some that grew very compactly, being strikingly different in appearance from the usual spruce with its long branches.

Variations in the color of foliage have also been given attention and have observed variations from bud sports in the wild specimens of *A. Douglasi* and *A. amabilis* that were of interest. In particular I have seen a single branch in a wild species (a bud sport) that would droop several feet below all the other branches. Such a branch may generally be propagated by grafting or from cuttings, and trees having this habit may thus be developed. There are numerous

YELLOW PINE

There are said to be more species of conifers in California than in all the rest of the world, and the very best of these, from the standpoint of the lumberman, is the yellow pine, here shown. Note the absolutely straight trunk, holding almost the same size to a great height. Observe, also, that this is a very large tree, although not, of course, competing with the giant Sequoias and the redwoods.

corresponding variations in cypress and other conifers grown from the seed.

The Douglas spruce is a common California form that is quite variable. This has exceptional interest, because it is a tree of very rapid growth. In many cases where a tract of land has been burned over or the trees have been cut off, there will spring up what at first appears to be a growth of oaks alone. But in fifteen or twenty years the growth of Douglas spruce will entirely overshadow the oaks, ultimately destroying them altogether, and presenting yet another illustration of the practical operation of natural selection.

But there is a very great variation among the individuals of the different species of conifers as to rapidity of growth. So there is fine opportunity for the experimenter to select the more rapid-growing trees, and thus to develop a race of timber trees of very exceptional value.

The experiment is not difficult with the Douglas spruce (*A. Douglasi*) as it bears seed while quite young, particularly when the trees stand by themselves. The seed remains in the cones for some time, to mature so that it may be collected at any season of the year. The seeds germinate readily, the seedlings may be easily transplanted, and in general this is one of the easiest conifers with which to work. The reasonable hardiness of the tree and its adaptation to all soils and climates are further merits that commend it to the attention of the plant developer, whether he have in mind a tree for ornament or for reforestation.

The experimenter should know, however, that the seed of the *Abies,* unlike that of the redwood and some other conifers, retain their vitality for a short time only. If attention is given to the securing of fresh seed, the experiments can scarcely fail to go forward successfully.

There are, of course, almost numberless other species and varieties of conifers that hold out inviting opportunities for the plant developer. A beginning may be made with almost any varieties that chance to grow in your vicinity, and the facility with which the different varieties may be reproduced, together with the wide range of variation, offer opportunity for selection and insure interesting developments, provided you have sufficient patience to wait for them.

SOME DECIDUOUS FAVORITES

But if there are no broad-leafed trees that quite equal the hardest of the conifers in capacity to withstand cold and to draw nourishment from sandy or rocky soils under disheartening conditions, there are a few tribes of deciduous trees that make at least a commendable effort to rival them.

Notable among these is the birch. But the beech, oak, maple, hickory, and walnut also have representatives that are able to withstand the winter in regions where the mercury freezes.

All of these have a certain importance as ornamental trees, but in the main they are valued rather for their timber, and we have dealt with them when we spoke of forest trees.

There is a considerable company of trees of less hardy character that nevertheless are resistant enough to thrive in the streets, parks, and gardens of our Northern States if given a certain amount of protection, even though some of them could not make their way in the wilds in competition with the hardy tribes just mentioned.

These trees are less hardy than the others, presumably because they migrated a little more rapidly in the old days of changing climates and kept far enough away from the ice sheet to be able to retain something of their taste for tropical conditions. They not only retained the broad leaf system, but some of them also retained or developed the habit of bearing handsome flowers—a habit that would have served

THE JUDAS TREE OR RED-BUD

This is a hardy tree of very wide distribution, the eastern species thriving from New York to Florida. There are three other species, one indigenous to Europe, the second to Japan, and the third growing along the Pacific coast. Interesting breeding experiments might be made by combining the various species. The tree is peculiarly attractive at the flowering time, early in the spring, before the leaves appear.

small purpose for the conifers, since insects could not thrive in cold regions where they remained to battle with the elements.

Doubtless the most interesting of these trees that escaped destruction by flight, and the one that has maintained most fixedly the traditions of the Mesozoic era, is the tulip tree (*Liriodendron*).

This beautiful tree, with its unique broad glossy leaves and handsome flowers is now the lone representative of its genus. One species alone survives as the remnant of a tribe that flourished abundantly in the Mesozoic Age. This species made its way to what is now the southern part of the United States, and has kept up its aristocratic traditions throughout intervening ages of such vast extent that it staggers the mind to attempt to grasp their significance.

The thoughtful person cannot well escape a feeling of awe as he stands in the presence of this representative of a race that in the main was gathered to its fathers at a time when the ancestors of man were perhaps still progressing on all fours.

But, traditions aside, the tulip tree of to-day is a thing of beauty, prized for itself, regardless of its ancestry. It makes a fine tree for avenue,

dooryard, or park, and it may be grown as far
north as New York and New England.

Being a monotypic tree, one would not expect
it to show very great variation. But no very
keen powers of observation are required to see
that the tulip trees are not identical, and doubtless their variation is enough to afford opportunities for interesting experiments, though
there is nothing on the earth at the present time
with which to combine them.

Exceptional interest should attach to a line of
experiment in which the plant developer is dealing with racial traditions of such antiquity and
such fixity. Meantime, the fact that the tree has
a beautiful flower gives opportunity for a line of
experiment that is usually possible only among
herbs and bushes, inasmuch as most of our trees,
as the reader is well aware, are wind-fertilized,
and hence do not bear conspicuous blossoms.

There are several other trees, however, that
resemble the tulip tree in the matter of blossom
bearing, and that are not altogether unlike it
in general appearance, some of which have corresponding interest, being representatives of
ancient forms, even if not quite rivaling the tulip
tree in the length of their unmodified pedigrees.

The catalpa and the magnolia may be named
as perhaps the chief representatives of these

flowering trees. Both of these are represented by several species, and the representatives of each are subject to considerable variation.

There are at least two distinct hybrid catalpas, involving three species, and I have noted great difference in the rapidity of growth of seedling catalpas; also variation in color and abundance of flowers, in length of seed pods, and in manner of growth of the trees themselves, some being much more upright than others, and I have observed magnolia hybrids also, and have thought it matter for surprise that there are not more of them, for the trees are readily cross-fertilized. Doubtless the fact that different species bloom at different seasons largely accounts for the relative infrequency of natural crossing.

There is an opportunity to work with the catalpa, and I could scarcely mention a plant that seems to me to give better promise for experiments in crossing and selection than the great and varied family of magnolias.

If the seeds are planted while fresh, they germinate readily. The seedlings are easily raised—almost as easily as apples or pears.

Among the magnolia seedlings now growing on my grounds, there are some that will grow three or four feet the first season, while others grow only as many inches. Some have a branch-

THE HYBRID ELM

In the background, the hybrid elm and the Chilean pine. At the left, the selected strawberry plants that remain after the bed has been thoroughly thinned. In the middle ground, a row of teosinte.

ing habit, and others form an upright growth. The leaf varies in breadth and length and in general appearance. Some are early bloomers and some are late bloomers. There are different shades of flowers. All in all, there is abundant opportunity for interesting experiments in selective breeding.

Among other interesting deciduous trees, all of which afford ready opportunity for experimentation, are the acacia and its relative the locust (the seeds of both of which may best be made ready for germination by boiling), the alders are quite variable and with which I have made interesting experiments; the ash, which affords excellent opportunities for hybridization, and is especially promising for timber; and the hawthorn, which has attractive flowers and fruit that are subject to a wide range of variation, and which has exceptional interest because of its not very remote relationship with the great tribe of trees that furnish our chief orchard fruits.

The names of the dogwood, the pepper tree, strawberry tree, and numerous others might be added, but regarding each of them substantially the same thing might be said. All offer excellent opportunities for selective breeding; but few or none of them have been extensively worked with hitherto.

THE FINEST OF ORNAMENTAL TREES

There is one peerless tree, however, that I must single out for a few added words of special mention in concluding this brief summary of some of the more notable among the ornamental trees.

This is the elm, a tree that occupies a place apart, having scarcely a rival when we consider the *ensemble* of qualities that go to make up an ideal ornamental and shade tree.

Whoever has visited an old New England village, and has walked through the corridors of elms or looked down the vista of streets arched over by the interlocking branches of the rows of trees on either side, will not be likely to challenge the preeminence of this tree. Nothing could more admirably meet the purposes of a shade and avenue tree.

The English elm, which is a more compact grower than the American species, has been widely planted in California. But the American elm thrives here also, although not native to the coast, and it is much less subject to insect pests than is the European species; also the English elm is stiff, and quite lacking in the graceful lines that the American elms so naturally assume.

There is a very wide range of variation among American elms, notably in the size of the leaves, and the openness or compactness of growth, and in the weeping habit.

The variation is so great that it is never wise to plant a row of seedling elms along a street or roadside. It is much better in the interest of uniformity to secure trees that have been grafted.

The slippery elm, which grows in the same regions with the common American species, is a tree of more compact growth, but on the whole not to be compared with the other species. There are natural hybrids, however, between the American elm and the slippery elm that exceed either parent in size, and sometimes are of surpassing beauty.

The largest tree that I have ever seen in New England, and perhaps the largest elm that ever grew, was one that grew in Lancaster, my boyhood home, and which I have every reason to believe was a hybrid.

As I was born and brought up under the elm, I have naturally an affection for them greater perhaps than for any other tree. Branches were once secured of the gigantic hybrid, while on a visit to my old home, and brought to California and grafted on roots of a seedling of the American elm on my home place at Santa Rosa.

When this grafted tree was only fifteen years old it was two and a half feet in diameter. Its hybrid character is obvious to all botanists who have examined it and as the original giant Lancaster elm has since been destroyed by a passing hurricane, I now have the only representative of it still living.

I have not experimented further with the elm in this direction; but the grafted tree that thus reproduced the personality of the giant elm in the shadows of which I passed my boyhood—a souvenir that links the home of my mature years with the home of my ancestors—is a source of perpetual pleasure.

PERSONAL AND HISTORICAL

Sketch of the Author by His Sister
Emma Burbank Beeson

THE town of Lancaster, Massachusetts, is
one of the most picturesque in all New
England. Its unsurpassed scenery is of
the English type, a wealth of queenly elms of
wondrous size and beauty gracing its highways
and meadows. The gently flowing Nashua
River; quiet, wood-encircled lakes; sparkling
springs of pure, sweet water; rich grassy intervals and gracefully sloping hills—all lend a peculiar charm to its rare beauty. The treasures of
mountain, field, and forest are there; the blue of
the fringed gentian, the sumac's fire, and the
thousand varied forest tints unite with the wild
flowers, berries, fruits, and nuts to make life
enjoyable. Although there may be something
of restraint in New England life, there can be
no monotony in a land of such charmingly diversified scenery, and oft-changing seasons. Spring
with its promise-bursting seed and budding

flower; summer with its fullness—blue sky and
green grass; autumn with the Indian summer's
myriad colored leaves, and harvest time; winter
with snowdrifts and merry sleigh bells, ice-clad
trees, and warm, cheery sociability—each season
has its own attractions.

Lancaster is rich, too, in historic lore: more
than two and one-half centuries have passed since
the town was settled by white men. Before Lex-
ington, Bunker Hill, or Philadelphia and the
Liberty Bell had been called into existence;
before there was any dream of the mighty possibilities of this Western Continent, a tract of land
ten miles long and eight miles wide, in the valley
of the Nashua River, was purchased in the
year 1643 of the Indian chief, Sholan, sachem
of the Nashaways or Nashawogs, a tribe
whose wigwams were located near Washacum
Lake.

In the year 1653, there being nine families in
the settlement, the township was incorporated
under the name of Lancaster.

The soil and climate were not hospitable to
ignorance and indolence, and the great West of
to-day owes much of its prosperity to the high
ideals of these pioneers who laid a sure foundation for future development; and from Maine to
California there is scarcely a community but has

felt the impulse of the high ideals of the sober, industrious New Englander.

Since the settlement of Lancaster our national history has been the most inspiring and luminous in all human experience, and this town has not failed to furnish its full quota of names of those who in peace and in war have stood high in the annals of the commonwealth and the nation.* This is also true in the world of science and of letters.† Only a few of the great mass of mankind stand above the others and impress one with the sense of their individuality. The same is true of cities and towns, and when Athens, Edinburgh or Concord is named, there is presented a distinct picture of life with a quality of its own, like a face of Van Dyck, or statue of Phidias. The town of Lancaster, Massachusetts, by general consent has such an individuality. A typical New England home in this beautiful town was the Burbank homestead—the large, square brick house standing well back from the street beneath the swaying branches of a great elm tree. It was a sort of rendezvous for ministers, lecturers, and teachers, and was charged with intellectual activity. Into this home on the seventh

* History of Lancaster, by Abijal P. Marvin, published by the town in 1879.

† A Bibliography of Lancastriana, by Henry S. Nourse, published in 1901, compiled for the Public Library.

day of March, 1849, was born the thirteenth child
—Luther Burbank.

The year 1849 was, in New England, an
active, busy year, as gold had just been discovered in California, creating such an excitement
as—with the single exception of that occasioned
by the memorable Boston Tea Party in 1774, and
the consequent events—probably had not been
equaled in American history. During this and
the two following years many were preparing to
cross the plains in quest of gold.

Such was the environment into which Luther
Burbank was born. His welcome was perhaps
made more tender by the fact that the little
brother and sister who had just preceded him
had been early excused from the school of life
and called away from its stern discipline. When
this frail sensitive child entered the home, older
brothers and sisters, as well as parents, rejoiced
at his coming.

A quiet, serious child, my brother's most
noticeable trait was a love—almost a reverence
—for flowers. A blossom placed in the baby
hands would always stay falling tears. Flowers
were never destroyed by him, but if, perchance,
one fell to pieces, his efforts were always attempts to reconstruct it. Flowers were his first
toys and, when he was old enough to toddle

about, became his pets. Especially dear to his
heart was a thornless cactus (*Epiphyllum*)
which he carried about in his arms, until in an
unhappy moment he stumbled and fell, breaking pot and plant. This was his first great
sorrow; although by care the plant was made to
flourish again. Trees and flowers were especially abundant near our home, and wandering
among them was a pastime he greatly enjoyed.
No child ever entered more fully into the heart
of nature. From my brother's writings I glean
the following reminiscences of his childhood:

"From a distinctly remembered incident I
must from the first have been of an investigating turn of mind. The first thing that was fixed
in memory happened in this way: my good
mother, conforming to one of the customs of
old New England days, had just finished preparing a large quantity of 'fried cakes,' and had
placed the boiling fat upon the floor in the
rear of the stove. Apparently it was a great
mystery to me how the hot fat could change
the sticky, unpalatable dough into the brown,
crisp—and evidently to my infant fingers—
irresistible 'doughnuts.' So, when mother's back
was turned, I 'hitched' along, as children do before they learn to walk, personally to investigate
the subject, and removing the lid from the ket-

tle thrust my fingers well down into the almost boiling fat. Distinctly do I remember the pain that followed, and also the sympathy of parents and neighbors extended in this trouble.

"This incident is mentioned partly to show that young investigators have their trials as well as older ones, especially if they strike out along new lines of thought or action for themselves. I have had reason later in life to know this holds true in all cases where original investigations, along any line, are undertaken. The pioneer in any new line of thought is usually first ridiculed and frowned upon; then abused; later endured and pitied; and often afterward accepted as an oracle. This can be explained satisfactorily: The partisan does not think deeply, but is prompted almost wholly by prejudice, and is always ready to rail at and ridicule any innovation, whether good or bad. Intelligent men and women suspend judgment until they can have an opportunity to weigh evidence, and dispassionately decide for themselves whether any proposition advanced is true or false. Unreasoning ignorance may be a necessary check upon us all; for envious, jealous, and ignorant enemies are often our best friends in disguise.

"Every man and every woman must meet some of them sooner or later in life, and each personally learn the vital lesson that these friends in disguise are the necessary tests of character and purpose. Thus folly, stupidity, ignorance, envy, and jealousy frequently are made to work for special as well as the general good.

"The next incident indelibly traced on the rapidly moving but invisible film of the soul, as the sum of individual environments is impressed upon the great heredity spirit of the race, occurred soon after—and this time, too, the trouble was caused by an original investigator. My nature-loving mother, while gathering the big, scarlet, luscious, wild strawberries, growing abundantly over the fields near our home, had carefully placed me on a dry spot among the late June grasses, when a mischievous tame crow, belonging to one of our neighbors, swooped down alongside and began pulling hard at my unprotected toes; the pain and fright were most distressing as the crow industriously applied his sharp beak to my tender toes, and by the most earnest persuasion I could not induce him to relinquish his hold. By repeatedly perforating the warm June atmosphere with shrieks, help came and the black rascal was prevailed upon to quit."

Our home was about three miles north of Lancaster village, just off the main road to Harvard;

father was an unusually prosperous farmer and
manufacturer. Besides his farming interests,
with a large family, he found it necessary to
engage in manufacturing. On the farm was an
extensive bank of splendid clay; and as pottery
then was in great demand he engaged in its
manufacture. This business was carried on for
several years; but later the mammoth manufacturing paper and textile plants were established
in the vicinity, which created so great a demand
for brick that he found it profitable to establish
a brickyard on the farm; and as it takes wood
to burn brick he began buying woodlands, of
which he acquired large holdings. His judgment of the value of growing woodlands was
good, and he employed a large number of men
each summer to make and burn the brick, some
of whom were engaged during the winter in
chopping and hauling wood, and in hauling the
brick by teams to the railroad stations, or deliv-
ering them to the various towns and cities within
fifty miles of the farm. Luther, and a younger
brother, Alfred, when quite young, perhaps only
six or eight years of age, used to drive the oxen
with loads of brick to Clinton, Lancaster village,
Harvard, Fitchburg, Groton, Leominster, Shir-
ley, Sterling, Acton, and other near-by towns.
The Lancaster Gingham Mills, the Washburn

and Moen Wire Works, the Crocker Burbank Paper Mills, and many hundreds of other brick buildings in Lancaster and the towns surrounding were furnished from this source. Father also furnished much material from the farm and woodlands for the powder and paper mills in the neighboring towns; and for Luther it was a great treat, when taking material to the carpet, paper, cloth, and wire manufacturers, to see the wonderful processes employed in transforming the raw materials into such intricate forms of utility and beauty.

Samuel Walton Burbank, our father, was a man of sterling integrity, scholarly tastes, strong convictions, and unusually good business ability. He was very indulgent, and fond of his children, and gave to each the best education within his power. He was always sincere, and much respected by his neighbors, and greatly enjoyed his associations with them. He served in important offices in the government of the town, but generally preferred his home and business relations to outside engagements.

Mother, whose maiden name was Olive Ross, was an active and intelligent woman, looking after her household duties with scrupulous care. She seemed always to know where everything wanted could be found, and, better still, she was

OLIVE ROSS BURBANK,
LUTHER BURBANK'S
MOTHER

This picture was taken when she was past ninety years of age. She lived to the age of ninety-six years and six months. The last twenty-five years of her life were spent in the Burbank home at Santa Rosa. She was at all times a source of inspiration and encouragement.

usually able to find it. Being naturally expert
in reading human character, she was of great
assistance to father in his business, as he employed much help and dealt with men of all
classes and of various nationalities. Indeed, she
was truly a helpmate to her husband in all
respects. She was fond of flowers, and with
all her other numerous duties had the home surrounded by them. After coming to California
she lived in Luther's home, active and interested
in all of his work until her death in December,
1909, at the age of nearly ninety-seven.

We first hear of the Burbanks at Lancaster,
Lancashire, England, from which place five
Burbank brothers emigrated to America. We
find by the customhouse records at Boston, Massachusetts, that Joseph Burbank came in the
ship *Abigail* from London in 1635, and that
John Burbank, from whom our family descended, was made a voter at Rowley, Massachusetts, in 1640.

Father's mother was Ruth Felch, originally
from Wales. Mother's family—the Rosses—
came from Scotland: "This was a great and
illustrious family in the time of Kings Robert
and Bruce. Among the ancient and noble
houses of Scotland none perhaps ever held
a higher place in the annals of the country

than the Rosses of Ross-shire, descendants of the ancient Earl of Ross. As early as the year 1000 A. D., the chiefs of Ross were powerful nobles, equal to any in Europe, and at one time their wealth and influence were only equaled by those of the King of Scotland himself. In fact, they were connected with the royal family by a number of marriages, as shown in the coat of arms of the earls of Ross which were taken from the shield of the King to show that they were children of the royal house. Of the descendants of the earls of Ross, the house of Balnagown, the first laird was Hugh Ross of Rarichies, second son of Hugh, fifth earl of Ross. From the house of Balnagown sprang many noted branches of the family, and in tracing the descent of these branches almost every event of importance in the history of Scotland is touched upon. Rev. George Ross of Balblair, Ross-shire, the emigrant, was the progenitor of a line of illustrious men who have made as deep impress upon the pages of American history as his ancestors had done in Scotland. He descended from the ancient earls of Ross in a direct line through the houses of Balnagown, Shandwick, Balmachy, and Balblair. Though the great feudal power of the family had been broken, great wealth still remained in the parent house of Shandwick and Balnagown. Col. George Ross, one of the signers of the Declaration of Independence, was of this family. The descent from Malcolm (1165-1214), first earl of Ross, is traced through the earls of Ross, to the family in America."*

The name of mother's mother was Burpee, a family of French descent. Thus it will be seen that our ancestry, like that of most people in America, is made up from many nationalities.

The Burbanks were generally farmers, paper manufacturers, railroad men, teachers, and clergymen; while on the Ross side the ancestry were more often merchants, mechanics, and horticulturists. Few families of New England have more reason to be proud of a prestige so well and universally sustained as the Burbanks; few families have been so eminently represented in the learned professions, in civil enactments, in military stations, and in all public reforms.

Professor Levi Sumner Burbank, a cousin, who lived with us part of the time, was a personal friend and associate of Louis Agassiz, and in rambles with him Luther's love of nature was greatly increased, as he knew the names of the rocks, flowers, and trees. This cousin was at one time principal of the Lancaster Academy, and

* Clan Ross in America, 1914.

was one of the first members of the American
Association for the Advancement of Science.
He wrote a number of books on scientific subjects, one of which was entitled "The Eozoonal
Limestones of Eastern Massachusetts." He
frequently took long trips with Agassiz to
places of scientific interest; west to the copper
mines of Michigan, where Agassiz had invest-
ments; south to the Mammoth Cave, and to
other points of interest to naturalists. He was
also at one time Curator of Geology of the Boston Society of Natural History, and had a large
and well-selected geological collection. In this
way Luther came to know much of Agassiz and
his work.

Our Lancaster home was not far from that of
Ralph Waldo Emerson at Concord. The family
were all greatly interested in the characters of
Lincoln, Emerson, Webster, Sumner, Agassiz,
Thoreau, Channing, the Beechers, the Fowlers,
the Fields, and the Alcotts, with several of
whom father was personally acquainted.

We were brought up under the strict New
England régime, though our parents were exceedingly reasonable and indulgent. They did
not think it well for children to roam the fields
and woods on Sunday; yet, because of Luther's
love for the birds, flowers, and trees, often

allowed him to go out on Sunday afternoons and roam in the fields among the trees, birds, brooks, and flowers. The memory of these rambles is yet recalled by him with much satisfaction.

On our farm were extensive peat meadows, on which several acres of cranberries were growing. It was of great interest to Luther to see the men rake off the cranberries by the bushel with cranberry rakes, instead of picking them by hand as other berries are gathered. When he was twelve to fourteen years of age it was thought best to flood the meadows to increase their productiveness. A large trout stream ran through the meadow and Luther conceived the idea of damming it, ostensibly to increase the crop of cranberries, but chiefly for the purpose of providing a fine place for skating—an amusement of which he was very fond. Much hard work was done by him through the October and November days in building the dam which later flooded not only father's cranberry meadows, but a great number of acres adjoining. One of the happiest days of his life was that on which he first saw this great sheet of water where none had been before. Flashboards had been prepared to raise the water at the dam as desired, and during the winter when the snow fell, covering the ice, it was only necessary to add a board to raise the water above the snow to make the whole surface a glassy sheet again, upon which scores of young people had great sport with sleds and skates.

During the long winters father, with Luther and Alfred, often visited the woodlands where the men were employed in chopping and preparing the wood for burning the brick during the following summer. During the summers Luther used to help in the brickyard (generally against his will) in turning numerous, long rows of brick on edge to dry, but whenever opportunity was afforded, he engaged in building windmills, water wheels and steam engines, making statuary, pottery, etc., carrying on a variety of chemical and other experiments that were of more interest to him than turning brick on edge —a very arduous task when well done, and one that always resulted in sore hands and aching back and legs.

A great source of delight to him were the excursions into the woods in summer time among the waving boughs of maple, walnut, chestnut, birch, beech, aspen, oak, and pine. These wood roads wound through great gardens of mountain laurel with glistening leaves and magnificent crimson, pink, and white blossoms; near by was Cumbery Pond, with its waters well stocked with fish; the old "Slate Quarry"; the "Cinnamon Roses"; the great "cold spring"; and a hundred places of interest and pleasure to our childhood. Nor were the woods less attractive in autumn, with their gorgeous tints, rustling fallen leaves, among which we found the nuts of the beech, butternut, hazel, hickory, and chestnut. A ride on the great rude wood sleds in winter among the ice-clad or snow-laden trees was no less delightful.

Chemistry and mechanics were of great interest to Luther. First the attic, containing the little wooden cradle, painted blue, in which so many tired little ones had been hushed to sweet slumber, the old spinning wheel, and ancient and dilapidated furniture allured him. Later experiments were begun in the backyard with an old tea kettle, and the neighborhood was aroused by an untiring steam whistle. These experiments continued until he had perfected a miniature steam engine, which he afterward sold to be used in propelling a small pleasure boat.

An extreme shyness, the result of a delicate physique and undue sensitiveness, often caused Luther to be misunderstood and to shrink from notice, bearing undeserved reproaches in silence. When one of the many visitors at our home looked at him across the table he would often slip off his chair and run out of doors, not relish-

ing too critical observation. Even before he
could count, if he saw more places set at the
dinner table than he could ascribe to the members of the family, he would quietly say to
mother: "I don't want any dinner to-day."

Habits of observation and classification resulting in the power to individualize were early
developed. Luther knew more than anyone
else about the apples in the orchard, the nuts in
the woods, and the wild berries on the hillside and
in the meadow grasses. He made friends of
birds, insects, and animals, and rocks, trees, and
clouds did not escape his notice. An artist and
poet in heart, no doubt even at an early age
dreams were cherished of a great life work,
dreams which a natural timidity caused him to
hide within his own consciousness.

Each winter brought many noted lecturers to
the forum in Lancaster. An especially deep
and lasting impression was made upon Luther's
life by a series of lectures delivered there by
Professor Gunning, on astronomy, physical
geography, geology, mineralogy, palæontology,
and other kindred subjects, not supposed to be
especially interesting to a child.

Luther's first experience in school life was in
a little red schoolhouse, located about one-half
mile from our home. On his first day the super-

intendents, or "committee men," as they were called, visited our district, which was Number Three, nicknamed "Gotham." The next district adjoining Number Three on the north bore the euphonious name of "Skunk's Misery." The other districts had similar distinctive names, such as "Ponakin," "Babel," "Deer's Horn," "The Neck," and others which cannot now be recalled. On that first day at school the rest of the pupils seemed to have no trouble in reading off promptly, but it was a terrible ordeal to Luther, and when his turn came he boohooed, and was excused. During the first winter, David, one of our older brothers, generally took him on a hand sled to school, after mother had tied a warm, woolen tippet about his neck and placed some thick, red and white woolen mittens upon his hands. After the first day at school, most of his troubles were over, though the big boys sometimes used to "yaff" at him.

In this school sister Jane, brother Herbert, and cousins Myra and Calvin, were at times his teachers. The course of study was the usual one followed by the schools at that time. His opinion, as now expressed, is that he began the study of arithmetic, grammar, and algebra altogether too early in life, as most children are required to do to-day; although they are now prepared to approach the subjects by successive steps more natural and reasonable. These studies were never a pleasure to him until he was much older; but geography, word analysis, and later geometry, pencil and crayon drawing, and the languages were an unceasing delight.

At the Lancaster Academy, a high-grade preparatory school, there were usually about seventy-five to one hundred and twenty-five pupils, local, and from all over New England and many Western and Southern States. Here, as at the district school, Luther was a favorite with teachers and schoolmates. As was the custom on Friday afternoons, the students were required to declaim, but owing to nervous timidity he could not by any possibility do himself justice in this trying ordeal. And not until recent years has he been able, with any degree of composure, to address an audience. In order to avoid these Friday afternoon ordeals, though standing unusually high in all other studies, he remained at home on the day for his turn in this exercise, notwithstanding the fact that it caused him no little regret to do so. The principal, though severe in government, was kindly, and after a time granted him the privilege of writing a composition each week instead of declaiming once a fortnight.

From that time on he enjoyed academic life most intensely. Free-hand drawing was very easy for him, and even after leaving school and while at work in the city of Worcester at woodworking and pattern making, he took lessons in drawing once a week from the well-known artist, Professor George E. Gladwyn, so long connected with the Massachusetts Institute of Technology, who had a large class in drawing and designing.

Father, observing that all Luther's leisure moments, before leaving the academy, were employed in building water wheels, steam whistles, steam engines, or something of the sort, concluded that he ought to be a mechanic. An uncle, Luther Ross, was superintendent of the woodworking department of the great Ames Manufacturing Company, which had plants at Worcester, Groton, and Chicopee Falls, Massachusetts. A place was secured for Luther in the factory at Worcester, where he was at first employed in turning the plowrounds, for which he received the munificent sum of fifty cents a day. Board was also fifty cents per day, and, as Sunday came once a week, he found himself fifty cents in arrears at the close of each week. Although he enjoyed the work, the compensation was insufficient, so his uncle granted him

the privilege of working by the piece instead of
by the day, and by special activity under this
arrangement he could make two or three times
as much as formerly.

After gaining some experience in this work
he contrived an improvement in the power turning lathe that enabled him to earn from ten to
sixteen dollars a day. With this good fortune,
he was greatly elated and gave himself to the
work with increased industry; but the clouds of
dust that came from oak lumber began to impair his health, and it was thought best that he
should leave the shop for a time. Later return-
ing to the Ames Works, he was again employed
at pattern making and wood turning for a short
time.

All this time his love for nature and out-of-
door life had not lessened. Letters written to
friends at home while employed by the manufacturing company at Worcester were full of
references to long walks, the beauty of sky,
trees and flowers, the song of birds, and the pip-
ing of the frogs. His fondness for studying
human nature dates back to these days at
Worcester, for in one of his letters at that
time he wrote: "I take great pleasure in
studying the hundreds of new faces which I
meet each day."

When Luther was twenty years of age, he decided that the physician's profession would be the most congenial as a life work, and so he began the study of medicine; the value of the knowledge thus gained in practical hygiene and physiology as applied to plant life can hardly be estimated; but father's death, occurring at this time, the purpose was abandoned, and the family moved to Groton—now Ayer, Massachusetts, where we lived two years. It seems that nothing was to turn Luther from his great life work; and having purchased seventeen acres in the village of Lunenburg for raising seeds and market garden products, he began definite experiments with plants, in which field he saw great possibilities.

It was here that the now world-famed Burbank potato was produced and numerous experiments inaugurated for the improvement of plant life which have been continued uninterruptedly until the present time. After spending three years in this work he moved to Santa Rosa, California, where he has resided since October 1st, 1875.

Although the time intervening between the date of his decision to come to California and the time for starting was short, not being more than sixty days, yet during that period he sold all his personal property; and the accounts of the business transacted had been so accurately kept that the total amount of these sales was found to be within a few cents of the amount of his annual appraisement. The same regard for system and accuracy in all the details of business which have ever characterized his methods were here shown. Meantime, besides settling up these matters, he had sent to different parts of California for copies of various newspapers, purchased and read several books on California, and interviewed several parties who had visited the State; and from this information he decided that northern California was probably the most suitable to his purpose for the production of improved forms in plant life.

Two older brothers were then living in Tomales, California—George, who came in 1854, and David in 1859. Having learned before coming to the State that the climate of Tomales, being close to the ocean, was too harsh for his experiments, after some hesitation between San Jose and Santa Rosa, he decided to locate in Santa Rosa. Sometimes he has thought that the work might have been slightly more advanced if he had settled in the larger town of San Jose, in the midst of the world's greatest fruit-producing section, but, on the whole, he has been satisfied with the choice that was made before leaving New England.

After preparing to go to California, and just before he left Massachusetts, the "Ralston Failure" occurred, which all old Californians too well remember. Friends advised him to change his mind on account of the reports of the greatly depressed conditions California was then experiencing, but having sold his property and made all arrangements for the change he was not to be deterred, and started overland in September.

The trip to California was made alone, with the money mostly obtained by the sale of the Burbank potato, which had been produced before and had been sold for one hundred and fifty dollars to J. J. H. Gregory, a prominent seedsman of Marblehead, Massachusetts.

On arrival in California, Luther had little with him, except some clothing, books, and garden seeds, and ten Burbank potatoes which Mr. Gregory had allowed him to take in order to get a start.

Santa Rosa was then a little village without a sidewalk; surrounded by wheat fields; no orchards, no vineyards, but few ornamental trees and very little employment for anyone except that of driving great teams of oxen or mules, in plowing with gang plows in the winter, or working with threshing crews in the summer. Luther's physical strength was not sufficient to take either of these positions. With little available means, in a strange land, far from home and friends, he met with hardships from which his sensitive nature recoiled, and which would have turned a less determined soul from its purpose. Letters written at this time to mother and sister in the old New England home contain no details of these hardships but are overflowing with enthusiastic descriptions of the beautiful scenery, flowers, trees, and birds, of the pure air and blue sky of the new land.

Seeking work, he let no opportunity pass by, often accepting that which was far beyond his strength; and doing all sorts of odd jobs. Once hearing that help was wanted on a building then in construction, he applied and was promised work if he would furnish his own shingling hatchet. He spent his little remaining money for one and reported for work the next morning only to meet with another disappointment, as the job had been given to another. Then he went to Petaluma where he worked through the winter and spring of 1876 in the nursery of W. H. Pepper, which was established in 1852, one of the first in California. Here, occupying a room over the steaming hothouse at night, and exposed to the damp soil and climate by day, his strength gave way, and he returned to Santa Rosa only to be laid low by fever. But for the kindly ministrations of a good neighbor his work might here have ended. A good woman, seeing his need, furnished him fresh milk from her family cow, and, without hope of reward, saved Luther Burbank, not alone to family and friends, but to the world.

A small piece of land was now rented and while working at carpentry during the day, he devoted the long summer evenings to preparations for starting a small nursery of his own.

With the nursery, the Burbank potato was advertised in a small way for seed. This helped out a little; he was also employed as collector of native California tree seeds for several American and European seed firms, and in this way became acquainted with most of the plants and trees that grow in this part of the State, the locality where they grow, the time of blooming, the time of ripening the seed and other particulars that have since been of considerable importance to him in his work.

No path had been blazed for his footsteps, for his work has no precedent, but as Copernicus

LUTHER BURBANK'S
BIRTHPLACE

This is the old Burbank homestead at Lancaster, Massachusetts. The walls were of homemade brick, sixteen inches in thickness. It was overshadowed with great weeping elms, and was a busy place and a peaceful, happy one for us children.

studied the movement of the stars through the apertures in the roof of an old barn back of the dilapidated house in which he lived, so Luther Burbank, while employed in the most commonplace tasks, was laying the foundation for future achievements.

In the summer of 1877, to his great joy, mother and sister (the writer) came to California to join him.

By the old sales books it is shown that the first year's sales in the nursery business amounted to fifteen dollars and twenty cents; the next year it was eighty-four dollars; the third year to about three hundred and fifty dollars; and at the end of ten years the quality of the trees and the reliability of the Burbank "Santa Rosa Nursery" became so widely known that he was selling over sixteen thousand dollars' worth of trees and plants per year.

After some years of this prosperity, he concluded that it would be safe to embark on the life work which he had laid out. Therefore the nursery business was sold in the fall of 1888 that he might devote himself exclusively to the production of new varieties of fruits, trees, and flowers.

Nothing but the most intense love for and a knowledge of the importance of this work could have induced him to have taken it up as a life work at this time when he was absolutely free to travel, see the world and enjoy himself.

Previous to this time, the Gold Ridge farm near Sebastopol had been purchased, from which the nursery stock was now removed and the ground covered by plants for experimental purposes. Many of these plants had already been experimented upon by him in definite lines for years. The work was amplified and extended, as time and space was now afforded, and plants from all parts of the world secured for still further development. Through many hundred faithful foreign collectors he had often obtained some wild plant whose economic possibilities had never been apprehended, and which might, perhaps, have remained unknown for ages. These plants, when brought under culture and careful observation, especially for promising variations, and by combinations with other wild or cultivated plants from other countries, have produced new plants possessing qualities both of enormous economic and scientific value, opening new fields for still further development in various useful directions. Often a certain experiment had been carried on to a point where it needed some quality more than any plant under cultivation had the power to add, but by judicious combination of some new, wild, related species, followed by selection, a most valuable acquisition has been produced. Curiously enough, a new Asclepiad, Solanum, Ampelidæ, Papaver, Prunus, Ribes, Rubus, or whatever was most needed, almost always came from some thoughtful, generous, unknown collector, in some out-of-the-way part of the world, whose name had never been known to him before, but who, apparently possessed of a subtle intuition, sent seeds of just the plant desired at the right moment. This has so often occurred that to him it is now a matter of expectation; he also has in several countries, which have not been thoroughly botanized, regular collectors; among the most active of whom was his highly esteemed collector in Chile, Señor José D. Husbands (now deceased), who has sent over six thousand five hundred new species for trial from the southern half of South America. For Luther Burbank he has scaled forbidden mountain peaks, waded rivers, visited islands, traveled through arid deserts, among rock piles and amid dangers from the native Indians who had never been subdued by the powder and balls of any people, but who have of late succumbed to a more insidious enemy—European and American whiskey. Later teachers, travelers, missionaries and even wild native North and South American Indians have been of great service.

On coming to California, my brother was surprised to observe the great number of varieties of fruits that could be raised with such ease when compared with raising them under eastern conditions; also with the fact that the varieties grown here were nearly all of eastern and foreign origin, few, if any, new varieties having been produced specially adapted to the new conditions. It seemed desirable that new varieties should be produced for these new conditions, and having done some work in that line before coming to California, he was prepared to take hold of it with a reasonable amount of confidence as to the outcome.

The fruits then existing seemed to him in various ways to be lacking in many important particulars, and this is true even to-day, although partially modified. For instance, some trees would bear large crops one year or, perhaps, two years in succession; then, from some cause—late spring frosts, heavy winds, too much rain at the time of blooming, or other more or less evident causes—the crop would be destroyed, thus making fruit raising, even here, somewhat of a "hit-or-miss" proposition.

One of the first things to attract his notice in the woods and along the creeks was one of our native lilies, *Lilium pardalinum,* commonly called the leopard lily. This flower is quite variable in a wild state, and this induced him to take up some of its best forms for study and cultivation in his own grounds.

At first, berries and lilies took much of his attention, and the experiments then made with these plants were the most extensive that had ever been made. At the same time he was growing apples, peaches, pears, plums, quinces, and numerous other fruits from selected seed by the hundred thousand each year, reserving only those that were most promising, which were grafted onto older fruit trees; by this means earlier fruiting resulted, thus making possible the testing of a vast number of varieties within the brief period of from two to four years. If anyone should think this a simple and inexpensive work, a little personal experience would disabuse one's mind of the idea, for it is all outgo, absolutely no income—millions of trees raised, just a few saved, none sold—none of them salable—and thus all but a few were consumed in enormous bonfires.

After about ten years of this work, it became plain to him that it must soon become imperative

either to cease the work, or reengage in the
nursery business in order to obtain means to carry
on the experiments; but the work had increased so
greatly that if another nursery should have been
started the experimental work would necessarily
have been neglected.   These perplexing conditions went on for some years.   At last both his
home place and the experiment grounds at Gold
Ridge were involved, and he had about decided
that it was best to curtail or perhaps entirely
abandon the experiments, at that time far more
promising than ever before.   The circumstances
were well known to many parties—in fact, to the
horticultural world generally.   Numerous friends
thought he should apply to some university, to
the United States Government, or to the State
of California for assistance, but he was unwilling
to accept any of these suggestions.   Finally, his
ever faithful friend and adviser, Judge Samuel
F. Lieb of San Jose, California, could endure the
situation no longer, and with Judge W. W.
Morrow of San Rafael, California, and Presi-
dent David Starr Jordan of Stanford University, all valued friends, everywhere honored and
revered as leaders in their respective professions,
and other esteemed friends at Washington, D.
C., without his knowledge, had made arrangements by which a grant or subvention should be

made by the Carnegie Institution at Washington for the continuance of the work. The terms involved in the first proposition did not meet with his approval, as it would have seriously and unnecessarily cramped the work. The next year (1904) a new proposition was made by the Carnegie Institution which gave him freedom, except that semiannual statements be made ($10,000 annually as long as agreeable to both parties); with serious misgivings he accepted the trust, and for five years worked under this arrangement. It being a difficult proposition to properly graft a branch of the young Carnegie Institution onto an established institution of more than thirty years' existence the expenses necessary to renew and extend the work and make arrangements for the preservation of the scientific data were large. And from the first he found it necessary each year to use an average of nine to twelve hundred dollars per annum *more* than the amount set aside for this purpose, the amount of labor and money expenditures required in producing these new creations being something astounding to anyone when first acquainted with the facts. The additional funds for continuing these experiments were obtained from the occasional sale of novelties, as before. At the end of five years this arrangement could no longer be endured and was dissolved, greatly to his satisfaction, leaving him again absolutely free from the long, weary, daily stenographic dictations which had been imposed during these five years.

Visitors were welcomed until he found it impossible to carry on the work and meet personally the rapidly increasing number, many of whom had journeyed thousands of miles to confer with him and to learn of his methods. Among these were men and women prominent in literature, art, education, science, finance, those connected with the governments of most foreign lands, and many whose names are familiar in song and story. Much of his inspiration has come from association with these choice spirits.

During the last ten years, however, he has been able to see but few of those desiring an interview. Words cannot express his sorrow that such should be the case, but it has been found necessary; otherwise the valuable work would lapse into utter ruin. Invitations to write and to lecture in this and other lands have necessarily been declined by him.

The success which attended these investigations in plant life has, in my brother's opinion, resulted from a life resolve made when he was eighteen years of age, that the search for *truth* was the one supreme ideal for man, regardless of dictum or creed of any sort, and through life he has found no reason to change the attitude then taken.

He believes that one's own life is the only true life to live; and that we should always remember that our brothers and sisters who are traveling the same road have the same rights and should have all the privileges we demand for ourselves; and that these privileges should be extended to our traveling companions in scales, furs, and feathers.

Although the name of Luther Burbank is familiar throughout the whole civilized world, and even where civilization is but partial, yet very few know how simple is his home life, or how strenuous is his work.

The little vine-covered cottage in a corner of the experiment grounds at Santa Rosa was his home for many years. Years of thought, planning, working and waiting, with insufficient laboratory and office room, with no trained assistants, he was thus compelled personally to keep his own accurate scientific records, his only financial resource was the occasional sale of novelties, the real cost of which was little understood. He listened quietly, patiently, and reverently to nature's lessons, and

THE OLD HOMESTEAD AS IT NOW APPEARS

The vines have almost taken possession of the place.

day by day his experiments were leading onward toward new plant creations which should beautify the earth and furnish food for the rapidly increasing population of the globe.

The cottage is now utilized for office purposes, for in the summer of 1906 the comfortable, spacious home which he now occupies was built, across the street and overlooking the home experiment grounds. Here, although the spirit of work pervades the atmosphere, the feeling of good cheer, peace, and tranquillity that ever accompanies the service that uplifts humanity, is very pronounced.

In person my brother is slight, almost frail, yet possessed of remarkable vitality and power of endurance. A face refined and spiritualized by the fires of enthusiasm and of suffering; the high, broad brow, and the soft brown hair now silvered, are in perfect accord with intense blue eyes that are keen to read to the very soul of things, yet lighten at every token of friendship and of honest appreciation of his work, or twinkle with shy humor. With its old-time simplicity his charm of manner lingers with one like the fragrance of flowers. Tender in his nature and overflowing with kindliness, he is strong in his principles and convictions and frankly unreserved, revered by associates, respected by employees, he is loved by those who know him best. Possessed of a strong individuality and intensity of feeling combined with extreme sensitiveness, he is compelled to carefully protect his vitality that he may devote all his strength to his chosen work.

A seeker after *truth* alone, he subscribes to no creed, belongs to no cult or sect, and refuses to wear badge or title, for only life sets the true seal to character. Unfettered by prejudice, always guarding against self-deception, laying aside theory, dogma, bias, he believes in himself and the sacredness of his mission.

A stroll among his growing plants, a day on the seashore or by some trickling mountain stream, are his chosen recreations, for his is a soul that feels the joy of the meadow, the laughter of the brook and sees unknown beauty in the most familiar objects.

He is intensely fond of music, but, as he is compelled to conserve his strength, seldom attends evening entertainments, and so insistent are the demands of his work that his vacations are few.

He is a rare conversationalist, using language clear and vivid, and ever since the time when his teacher granted him the privilege of writing an essay instead of declaiming for the Friday afternoon exercises at Lancaster Academy, writing has been a pleasure to him.

His catalogues, entitled "New Creations in Plant Life," which were published in 1893 and in succeeding years, are used as textbooks by many schools and colleges, and for reference by horticultural societies and experiment stations in this and other countries.

In 1907 the little book, "The Training of the Human Plant," was published and has found a very generous response from the public; it has been translated into several languages, put in form for the blind, and has become a textbook for the education of the young in thousands of schools and homes. His love for children makes it especially appropriate that his first printed volume be dedicated to the millions of school children under all skies, and that it be a plea for their better development. Especially appropriate, also, is the making of his birthday, March 7th, a legal holiday by the State of California, to be observed by the planting of trees and flowers.

In his marvelous conquest of plant life there has been no display and no magic, no elaborate appliances for research; only intuition, industry, skill, and patience; hands, eyes, and brain have been the instruments used in the interpretation and guidance of the laws of nature. A brief glance at what has been accomplished has been given, but, with the knowledge and skill attained, still greater work is now being done by him. Unswerved from his ideals by any hope of pecuniary reward, it can be truly said of Luther Burbank: the man is greater than his work.

THE STORY OF LUTHER BURBANK

AUTOBIOGRAPHY

IN examining a new and unexplored country, it is better to first take a broad, comprehensive, general view of the landscape before going into detail. Having secured our bearings of the new territory, we are then equipped for a more minute study of the nearer landscape.

We are now discovering how mobile all life, both static and dynamic, is under the deft might of mind. Each atom lives; there is no gulf between the quick and the dead and the elements of the human brain are found alike in the pebbles under foot and the blazing suns of space. All are alike subject to the universal attractions and repulsions of nature. True science and pure religion are branches from the same root; both are conscious and unconscious efforts of the human ego to adapt itself to the conditions of life. The foliage may well represent our daily life. The flowers of idealism lend a halo of beauty, fragrance, joy, love, and hope to life. The fruits formed through the more deliberate steps of science are also fundamental. The foliage is often injured by the mildew of insincerity and the caterpillars of avarice. The flowers, also, are all too often blasted and destroyed by the same means* and the fruit by worms at the core, which some of the useful but unwelcome facts of science bring to light.

The mind of man has sounded no limits to time or space. We are learning that all the varied forms and conditions which we know are intimately connected and interdependent upon the past conditions which have shaped their course and structure. The varying influences which have surrounded plants, animals, worlds or atoms have molded their varied characters and tendencies into their present make-up. This we may call heredity or stored environment. The more permanent aggregations with which we are familiar, like rocks, metals, air, water, and hundreds of others, seem generally very uniform and fixed in character; while, if these are assimilated and chemically combined into the forms of animals or trees, they are able to vary in aspect, in habit and character in order to adapt themselves to the varying conditions of life. If not

* Or the fungus of pride at the surface.

more pliable and alive than rocks and metals, they could not exist. Even the appearance and qualities of most chemical combinations which seem arbitrarily and permanently fixed, when combined and placed under certain new environments, may develop unsuspected characters and tendencies. Everybody knows that the characters of iron are more fixed than those of plants and animals. The characters and habits of iron, lime, soda, and hundreds of other chemical substances and compounds can be fully depended upon; they will act according to their inherent qualities. But these same chemical substances from which animals and plants are formed are so numerous and in such diverse combinations that their behavior is vastly more complicated and uncertain. The structures which we call plants and animals make use of the chemical forces of nearly every substance so far discovered in the universe.

Nature goes on giving birth to new nations, new peoples, which live their lives and disappear, to be replaced by others and others which follow, as far as we know, forever, or as long as this planet retains the conditions necessary to human and national life.

A good heredity from a clean upright ancestry is more to be desired than all the titles, honors

and wealth that earth can ever bestow. Cheer-
fulness, good health, thrift, and ability to concen-
trate and persist is a precious heritage. Millions
of "half men" are ushered into life, who are in
themselves wholly incapable of self-respect, self-
control, and self-determination, and only by some
unusual drug or other stimulant can they be
brought up to "concert pitch," so to speak, for
a brief space; in other words, up to the normal
average condition of ability to become self-supporting through life without infringing on the
normal rights of others, or to enjoy the ordinary
pursuits of life with relish and appreciation. The
man or woman who is endowed with a normal
nervous system rarely craves these various stimu-
lants, or, if so, is able to restrain the craving.
All this unusual stimulation, while giving a
present uplift, has the never-failing tendency
to pull downward toward the ever-increasing
desire for more and more. Will there ever be
any help for this? *Only one;* not through laws
based on punishment; not through religious
teaching; not through our ordinary educational
methods. It must and will come only through
methods similar to those that have produced and
are producing our best grains, fruits, and flowers.

Our present partial state of civilization has
been acquired by conscious and half-conscious

selection of the best and rejection of some of those unfit for breeding purposes. If we must have the stupendous pride and effrontery of placing ourselves above the ordinary everyday laws of the universe, we bring destruction upon ourselves, like the fool who builds his tinsel house upon the shifting sands. Education, training, and preventive measures are obviously essential makeshifts, but no amount of kind treatment or education can ever obliterate heredity defects from the race. Incompetents and criminals are born with these defects. Why not accept this fact squarely? The world will be a slaughter house—an insane asylum, and imbeciles and incompetents will walk the earth until the truth shall at last percolate into the minds of all that the unavoidable and unchangeable laws of nature which apply to the improvement of domestic animals and plants also apply especially to ourselves as well.

In the matter of my own heredity: though apparently frail in childhood and youth, I was in many respects fortunate in having the will and ability to work hard with head, hands, and feet, *averaging more than ten hours for each calendar day for the past sixty years,* and having lately sought for the causes of this state of affairs, find that all my ancestors and all my relatives on both sides as far as known, without exception have been, and are, industrious, happy, prosperous, respected, self-supporting citizens in their several communities. Not one of them, either on the Burbank or Ross side, have been deaf, blind, imbecile, insane, incompetent, intemperate, or addicted to the use of drugs or liquor; not one of them has ever been in any way a public charge or the inmate of any asylum; not one of them has ever been in jail, but that some of them might have been worthy of that position, I am not so certain.

Although my faithful father, good mother, and talented sister, Emma Louisa, had always been life's best inspiration, yet I had never known the companionship, joy, peace, and happiness of domestic life until I was sixty-seven years of age, when Miss Elizabeth Waters placed her heart and hand in my care for life. Since we have walked together, life has found a new meaning, and as friendly pals we romp, play, and labor in perfect accord. What an inspiration, help, and encouragement a good woman may be has been exemplified in the lives of millions of others, as well as my own. Much of my best work has been accomplished through her suggestion, counsel, advice, and help. The world will reward my "Betty" with the appreciation and love which she so well deserves.

A first cousin, Professor Levi Sumner Burbank, was a man of strong scientific proclivities, and was in part responsible for stimulating my love of nature, inasmuch as he lived with us at times, and I often rambled with him in the woods and gained from him a knowledge of the names of rocks and flowers and trees. Another first cousin on my mother's side, Silas Emerson Harthan, is acknowledged to have invented, constructed, and operated the first electric railroad ever seen on this earth. This was at Worcester, Massachusetts, in 1865, and hundreds of people who patronized this first of all electric roads are now living. He also invented the heel-making machines for boots and shoes, which did the work of one hundred men. The royalties for this invention were enormous. When he introduced the electric lights in Worcester, many of the inhabitants expected to see the city go up in smoke and perhaps with some reason, as these old-time electric lights used to flicker, sputter, sizzle, and shoot blue sparks. The bankers and business men gave it the "melancholy hoot" and declared it was the most dangerous thing ever invented. It was 1883 before the streets were again lighted with electricity.

MRS. LUTHER BURBANK

or "Betty," as we call her, who has helped greatly in the arrangement and construction of these volumes, for which she deserves your thanks.

Hartsook Photo

The Hereditary Background

I mention these scientific cousins as suggesting that there were certain proclivities that might in part account for the tendencies of a plant developer in the strains of my heredity. But, as what has just been said will further suggest, these were seemingly of a somewhat formal and technically scientific order, whereas the inspiration for my work has been found rather in an ardent love of nature. I desired to deal with the forces of life and mold the plastic forms of living organisms rather than to classify the fixed and immutable phenomena of dead ones, which would appear to be the province of the geologist.

Doubtless, however, the strain of interest in matters scientific that was evidenced in the geological proclivities of my Burbank cousin constituted an important hereditary element that, mingled with the more poetical and sympathetic elements of nature worship which were in the hereditary strains of my mother's family, rounded out the characteristics of an essentially practical plant developer who loved his task for the very doing of it, yet who never forgot that practical ends must be achieved.

My nature-loving mother, whose maiden name was Olive Ross, traced her ancestry back to the latter part of the tenth century, when a large tract of territory in Scotland, known as Ross-shire, was awarded to them for bravery in those ancient battles for supremacy.

I have always felt that my passionate love of flowers, which is said to have been manifested in infancy, was inherited from her.

Despite the poetical element in her temperament, my mother was eminently practical. Being of mature years when she married, she bore only five children, and outlived my father by many years, nearly reaching the century mark. She passed her declining days in my home at Santa Rosa, active to the very last and keenly alive to all that was going on around her.

The Physical and Mental Environment of Childhood

My father's two-hundred-acre farm was located about three miles north of the village of Lancaster, Massachusetts.

There I was born—at least so the great family Bible and the family traditions assure me—March 7th of the year 1849. And there my childhood and boyhood days were passed.

At that time the long-smoldering antislavery fires were preparing to burst forth. And just at the time when the great civic conflict was becoming more and more obviously inevitable, an intellectual and religious turmoil of world-wide scope was evoked by the pronouncements of Darwin and Wallace, which seemed to shake the fundamental notions as to man's creation, his past history, and his destiny.

These disturbing questions of national policy and intellectual and spiritual welfare were part and parcel of our everyday life in Lancaster during the years when I was passing from boyhood into adolescence.

As a child, I listened eagerly to the discussions long before I could more than half understand them, when on not rare occasions a visiting minister or lecturer was entertained at my father's table. Only the eager desire to hear these discussions overcame the awe of a strange face that led me always to dread the coming of a stranger even though I longed to hear his message.

I well recall how even in somewhat later years I cringed before the kindly scrutiny of our visitors and was dumb before their questions, though drinking in their words with eager interest so long as they were not addressed to me in particular.

I shall always feel that I was sent to school far earlier than was good for me. This, of course, was no fault of my parents. They but followed the traditions of the times.

That the rules of the three R's should be ground into the brain of the child while it was still at its most plastic stage, was accepted as unchallengeable.

The belief that the schoolhouse on every hilltop and the church in every valley constitute the landmarks of civilization was an ingrained fundamental of the New England tradition.

And so youngsters who should have been in the fields gathering flowers and reveling in the sunshine, drinking in the music of the birds and gaining strength and health for the tasks of mature life, were too often crowded into schoolrooms that in winter were overheated and ill-ventilated, and forced to the unwelcome and unnatural and harmful task of scanning pages of dots and pothooks and cramming their unwilling brains with formulæ, to their permanent detriment. Only on Saturday was there a respite. Later I attended the Lancaster Academy for a few years. This was a very high-grade preparatory institution.

Though not a university graduate, yet I had most unusual educational advantages and at the academy, after the first term, was always well up on the "Rank List" of the ten best students.

My years at the academy were very happy and useful ones, which later were supplemented by a series of drawing and painting lessons by Prof. Geo. C. Gladwyn, so long connected with the Massachusetts Institute of Technology at Worcester. He is now a very old man and I was lately pleased to receive a reminiscent letter from him. These supplemental lessons were taken just fifty-four years ago.

Two years of my nonacademic education were employed at wood turning and pattern making (from the age of sixteen to eighteen) at the Ames Manufacturing Company, Worcester, Massachusetts. The work was interesting and profitable, yet I preferred an academic education and the outdoor life which I had enjoyed on my father's farm, but the two years of intensely accurate measurements of forms, sizes, and adaptability have proved very useful in my later inventive work among plants. No doubt the world was open to me in the mechanical field as my two years so well proved; as during the time spent with the Ames Company, I helped to construct one of the first practical self-moving tractors for farm and road use ever operated. The tractor was propelled by steam and when completed moved itself through the streets of Worcester, Massachusetts, for exhibition and test, and attracted wide attention. It was designed and constructed for use in California, and I am told was still in use hauling produce and freight in the Sacramento Valley many years before the modern tractors made their appearance. This tractor had no steering apparatus of its own, but depended upon a span of horses attached to a long tongue to guide it, but the Worcester people were so delighted with this novel locotractor that two men offered to steer it, which they did readily, though horses were usually employed in this capacity.

The Lancaster Public Library at that time was the largest in all New England, except the Public Library in Boston, and one may rest assured that it was well patronized.

The Religious Environment

It is a little difficult for the present generation to gain a clear conception of the New England Sabbath of the time of my boyhood, and it may readily be inferred that the day thus given over to dolorous tasks was not one to which the child would look forward joyously.

Nor, for the most part, do those who were children in that generation look back upon the Sabbath day experiences with satisfaction.

At least they served the purpose, however, of supplying a church-going experience adequate for a lifetime.

Little did the good people who so sedulously led their flocks to church and subjected them to the bombardment of repeated sermons, suspect that they were cultivating an attitude of mind that would insure that the churches of succeeding decades should be nearly vacant. Indeed, they would have been horrified had they been told such a thing; yet I think we need not doubt that on the whole such was the influence of their well-meant efforts.

It adds to our understanding of the curiously archaic relation of the church to the community, even in that comparatively recent period, to reflect that it was obligatory in Lancaster a short time before for each family to contribute to the support of the Unitarian Church.

My father was not a Unitarian by profession, though his father was. However, father supplied sundry loads of bricks without charge for the building of a new Unitarian church, said to be the last one built under the old régime.

In subsequent years the law that made the Church practically a part of the civic organism had been repealed, and thenceforward people were allowed to follow their own inclinations in the matter of church contributions. But this severance of church and state, so to speak, did not so much represent a reaction against the doctrines of a particular church, as a general reaction against the obligatory recognition of any church whatever.

For there had come about in the course of one or two decades a most iconoclastic change in the attitude of mind of the leaders of thought throughout Christendom toward the tenets that had hitherto been thought essential to man's spiritual welfare.

Following the publication of Darwin's "Origin of Species" in 1859, the intellectual world was in a ferment, and nowhere was the influence of the new ideas more quickly felt or tumultuously argued than in New England.

I was ten years old when Darwin's iconoclastic document was promulgated, and hence I grew into adolescence in the very period when it was most ardently bruited. The idea that animals and plants have not originated through special creation but have evolved one form from another throughout long ages; and the logical culmination of that idea in the inclusion of man himself in the evolutionary chain—these are commonplaces to-day. They are familiar doctrines that might find expression from every orthodox pulpit.

But in those stormy days of the sixties, such ideas were not merely heretical—they seemed absolutely revolutionary.

If this new view were accepted, in the minds of a large proportion of those who expounded the subject in the early days in New England nothing good would remain.

Of course the history of the spread of this new doctrine duplicated the history of every other new idea. For the most part, people of the elder generation could no more change their old views and accept new ones than they could make over their stature or the color of their eyes.

But, on the other hand, we of the younger generation were quick to see the logicality of the new conception, and were not hampered in its acceptance by any cherished beliefs of a contradictory kind.

Not, indeed, that we children for the most part concerned ourselves greatly about the matter. We went through our regular task of Bible reading and churchgoing and learned our Sunday school lessons, just as we performed other tasks that we could not escape. But none the less were there instilled into the very substructure of our minds the essentials of the new manner of thinking, the new attitude toward the

world in which we live and all its organic
creatures.

And when in later years we went out into the
world and came to choose our own paths and to
adopt mental and religious garbs of our own
choosing, the subconscious influence of the new
teaching everywhere made itself felt, determining a receptive attitude of mind that presaged
the new intellectual era.

If ever there was a time when it was true that
"the old order changeth" in the profoundest
application of the words to the most sacred
beliefs of men, that time was the closing epoch
of the nineteenth century.

PLAY AND WORK

It is worth while to dwell on these less tangible aspects of the environment of boyhood,
because their influence was probably more important than that of many events that have to do
with the regular routine of the workaday world

As to that routine not much need be said,
because there was little associated with it that
was individual or characteristic or that was
largely influential in determining the activities
of my later years.

The recreations of such scant leisure hours as
the New England child of this period could find

were the usual recreations of childhood. I was rather too frail of body to enter with full enthusiasm into the rougher sports. But in general the sports and amusements of the New England child were of rather a subdued order, as became the intellectual atmosphere in which we lived.

Coasting and skating were among our most boisterous pastimes, and the more usual recreations included such functions as spelling bees and husking bees.

But the chief occupations of our leisure hours were of a more prosaic character than sledding or skating. My father was an unusually prosperous farmer, but he was also a manufacturer. With a large family, he found it necessary to supplement the resources of field and orchard.

And of course we boys were pressed into the service as soon as we were large enough to lend a hand at various of the simpler phases of brickmaking. It is recalled by my brother that I did not undertake the turning of brick, which is a work that is rather hard on delicate hands, with unusual enthusiasm. But, on the other hand, my brother Alfred and myself when quite young, perhaps only six or eight years of age, used to drive the oxen with loads of brick to Clinton, Lancaster Village, Harvard, and other near-by towns, and this part of the work I found thoroughly enjoyable.

When the time came for me to take up a definite occupation, I not unnaturally turned to one of the factories, the more willingly because of always having had the keenest interest in things mechanical.

At the Lancaster Academy, which I attended after gaining sufficient preliminary knowledge in the district school, I was particularly interested in free-hand drawing, which was found very easy, and had always an interest in designing. So my father, observing these tendencies, concluded that his son would be a mechanic.

I had not been long at work before the knack at contriving things mechanical came to my aid.

The company were pleased with my work and I might have remained indefinitely in their employ at a remunerative salary. But the clouds of dust that came from the oak lumber began to impair my health and it was thought best to leave the shop for a while at least. So my experience as a manufacturer of wood products ended.

CHOOSING A PROFESSION

I was always frail of body and of delicate physique, although wiry of build and not without good powers of endurance. But shop life further weakened me, and this led me to think of taking up medicine as a profession. On the whole it seemed to me that this would be most congenial, and I studied for a year with the intention of becoming a physician and have had occasion constantly to realize in later life how valuable this experience was. The knowledge of physiology and practical hygiene thus gained could many times be applied to the direction and interpretation of plant experiments.

It is quite possible that I should have continued my studies and have graduated in medicine had not the death of my father occurred at this time. This changed all our plans.

From earliest childhood my chief delight had been found in the study of nature and in particular in the companionship of flowers.

My earliest recollections center about the pleasure experienced in wandering in the woods, gathering wild flowers in summer, and in winter making excursions among the walnuts, birches, oaks, and pines that, viewed in perspective, seem to have been almost of the proportions of Sequoias, but which visits of later years revealed as trees of very ordinary proportions.

So it was perhaps inevitable that sooner or later an occupation should be chosen that would bring me hourly in contact with nature. But it was not until my twenty-first year that I entered specifically on the work, although of course I had been trained in all the tasks of the farmer, gardener, and fruit grower on my father's farm from earliest childhood.

I had all along been serving an apprenticeship that stood me in good stead now that the work of market gardener and seed grower was taken up as a business.

Yet it is not certain that I should have been led to put this knowledge to practical use at this time had it not been for the stimulation and fresh enthusiasm that came from the reading of an extraordinary book. This book was Darwin's "Animals and Plants under Domestication." The work was first published, it will be recalled, in 1868. It probably fell into my hands a year or so later. It came to me with a message that was not merely stimulating but compelling. It aroused my imagination, gave me insight into the world of plant life, and developed within me an insistent desire to go into the field and find the answer to the problems that the book only suggested. In particular it showed to me the plants of the field in a new light.

I had understood from Darwin's earlier work that all life has evolved from lower forms; that, therefore, species are not fixed and immutable, but are plastic, and amenable to the influences of their environments.

But I had not before understood to what an extent species of every kind all about us vary, and what possibilities of modification of existing forms are contingent on such variations. From that hour plant life presented to me a sort of challenge to test its capacities, to investigate its traits, to invent new ideals of growth and to endeavor to mold the plant in accordance with these ideals.

Thus, thanks to the inspiration of Darwin's work, my ideas were finally crystallized. The philosophical bent inherited from my father and the love of nature that I owed to my mother were now to work in harmony.

Guided by the practical instincts that were perhaps a joint heritage from both strains of these ancestors, and the love of mechanics that was only second to my love of nature, the inventive tendencies that had found earlier employment in the manufacture of steam engines and new turning devices were to be applied to the plastic material of the living plant.

Just where it all might lead no one could say. The field I was entering had been but little developed, but to my aroused imagination it seemed a field of picturesque possibilities.

Meantime, of course, it was necessary that I should gauge my enthusiasms in accordance with the practicalities. I must make a living, so purchased a seventeen-acre tract of land in the village of Lunenburg and began to raise garden vegetables and seeds for the market.

Something of the practical success achieved has been suggested here and there in connection with accounts of later plant experiments. In particular it may be recalled that I found ways of improving and cultivating sweet corn to meet the demands of an early market; and it may be said that in general my garden products were of exceptional quality.

Something has been said also as to the hybridizing experiments that were performed from the outset, including in particular the work with corn and with various races of beans. The experiments were by no means confined to these plants, however. I was like an explorer in a new and strange land full of inviting pathways and alluring vistas, and undertook to experiment in this direction and in that, giving every moment of spare time to the work of investigating the mysteries of plant life.

Every plant in the garden and every shrub and tree and herb in field or woods was examined now with new interest, always with first thought as to its tendency to variation. Where I had casually noticed before that individual flowers of a species differed in details as to form or color or productivity, accurate notes were now made of such variations and the query was raised as to whether they gave suggestion of the possibility of developing new races under cultivation.

Some of the early experiments were full of interest, and the knowledge gained through making them laid the foundation for later successes in plant development. But I had not proceeded far before it seemed clear that such experiments as were contemplated could not be carried out to best advantage in the climate of New England. My thoughts turned to California, where two of my half brothers had gone many years before. What was reported of the climate of the Pacific Coast region suggested this as the location where such experiments as were planned might best be carried out.

And when the first conspicuous success in the development of a new race of plants had been achieved, through the production of the Burbank potato—with the story of which the reader is already familiar—I determined at all hazards to move to California. With the taking of the practical steps that followed that determination, in the year 1875, a new epoch of my life began.

MY EARLY YEARS IN
SANTA ROSA

THE PERIOD OF BITTER STRUGGLE

WITHIN sixty days of the time when the definite decision to go to California was reached, I had sold my personal property and closed out my business at Lunenburg.

The business habits that my father had inculcated had been so systematically followed that there was little difficulty in closing up accounts.

But, although I had been fairly successful in the gardening enterprise during the three years that it had been under way, so much money had been spent on improvements that there remained but a small balance to my credit. At the moment, nothing could be realized on the farm. So in starting for California I was entering on a new field, backed by very little capital.

Meantime the well-known Ralston failure occurred.

Not feeling able to pay for a sleeping berth, which at that time was a rather unusual luxury, I was obliged to make such shifts as I could to gain snatches of sleep.

A generous lunch basket had been provided, and this served its purpose well, for the train was sometimes delayed for an entire day far out on the plains with no house in sight. Several times I had the pleasure of sharing my lunch with fellow passengers who would otherwise have suffered hunger.

At that time it was a common experience for axle boxes to become overheated by friction, and then it would be necessary to make long stops until repairs could be made. This, with numerous unclassified delays, made the journey longer, but added zest to the journey. At best, at that time it took nine days to cross the continent, and the contrast between the trains of that period and the luxurious expresses of to-day is notable.

EARLY DAYS IN CALIFORNIA

I have said that two older brothers were living in California. But I did not think Tomales, where they lived, a suitable place for the work in which I proposed to engage, because it appeared that this region, being close to the ocean, had a climate that was not well adapted to these experiments. I had been advised of conditions by letter, of course, from time to time, and had also read such books and articles dealing with California as could be found, so had rather clear notions as to what to expect.

The spirit of dogged persistency and of obstinate effort in the face of difficulties is a New England heritage.

Whatever the son of Puritan ancestors may lack, he is almost sure to have a full endowment of the basal instincts of "sticking to it.'

THE LAND OF PROMISE

I fully appreciated the natural advantages and beauties of the country to which I had come. Letters of the period, as preserved by my mother and sister, are filled with enthusiasm over the marvels of the new land. I may quote one of these letters as showing the impression that California made upon me, and the opportunities that it appeared to offer for carrying out my treasured project, if ever means could be found to make a beginning.

"Santa Rosa is situated," I wrote, "in a marvelously fertile valley containing one hundred square miles. I firmly believe from what I have seen that this is the chosen spot of all

LUTHER BURBANK AT THE AGE OF TWENTY-FIVE

the earth as far as nature is concerned. The climate is perfect, the air is so sweet that it is a pleasure to drink it in; the sunshine is pure and soft.

"The mountains which gird the valley are lovely; then the valley is covered with majestic oaks placed as no human hand could arrange them for beauty. I cannot describe it. (I almost cry for joy when I look upon the lovely valley from the hillsides.)

"California's gardens are filled with semitropical plants, palms, figs, oranges, vines, etc. Great rose trees, thirty feet in height, loaded with every color of buds and blossoms, in clusters of twenty to sixty, like a cluster of grapes (I would like to pile a bushel of them in your apron) climb over the houses. English ivy fills large trees, and flowers are everywhere.

"Do you suppose I am not pleased to see fuchsias in the front yards, twelve feet high, and loaded with various colors of blossoms? Veronica *trees,* geranium *trees;* the birds singing and everything like a beautiful spring day.

"The blue gum tree of Australia grows here seventy-five feet high in five or six years. Honeysuckles, snowberries, etc., grow wild on the mountains. There are so many plants more beautiful that they are neglected.

"I improve all my time in walking in every direction, but have seen no place which nature has not made perfectly lovely.

"I took a long walk to-day and found enough curious plants in a wild spot of about an acre to set a botanist wild.

"I found the wild yam which I hunted for so much in New England, also the yerba buena, a vine which has a pleasant taste like peppermint. (I send you a few leaves.) I also found a nut that no one seems to have seen before (have planted it), and several (to me) curious plants. I mean to get a piece of land (hire or buy) and plant it, then I can do other work just the same."

The intention to hire or buy a piece of land was not realized for a long term of months after it was thus confidently expressed. But the time came, after weary waiting, when it was found possible to hire a few acres. Then, although working at carpentry during the day, I was able to devote the long summer evenings to preparation for starting a small nursery.

I had come to California in October, 1875, and it was not until the autumn of the following year that the start in the line of work that had been planned was thus tentatively made. And even then my time of trial was by no means over. For, as has been said, no capital was available with which to push my enterprise, and it was necessary to feel the way, step by step.

To be sure I could have appealed to my brothers, and they would very gladly have helped me, but I was averse to doing this, both from an inherent sensitiveness about money, which is almost as universal a New England heritage as the Puritan conscience itself, and because I knew that my relatives, in common with such other people as knew of my project, were skeptical as to the practicability of such experiments in plant development as were contemplated.

Such skepticism was natural enough on the part of practical men, for the things that I hoped to do ran counter to all common experience. To think of changing the form and constitution of living things in a few years seemed grotesque even to many people who believed in the general doctrine of evolution.

It was not generally admitted at that time that the plants under cultivation had been conspicuously modified by the efforts of man.

And even those exceptional botanists who believed that the cultivated plants owed their present form to man's efforts were prone to emphasize the fact that the plants had been for centuries under cultivation and to question whether the modifications that could be effected in a single generation would have any practical significance.

So it seemed to most people who knew of my enterprise that it was a half-mad project and one that was foredoomed to failure.

Of course I had only enthusiasm, backed by the tentative results of early experiments in Massachusetts, to offer in response to such criticisms. So it seemed best to trust to my own resources, so far as possible, and prove my case according to my own method.

I would not be understood, however, as saying that my brothers did not give me friendly cooperation. On the contrary they were, as suggested, ready to extend a helping hand, and their aid was sought at the outset in the matter of the propagation of the Burbank potato, the ten tubers of which constituted, in my judgment, my most important tangible asset.

The ten potatoes were planted on my brother's place; and the entire product of the first season was saved and planted, so that by the end of the second season the stock of potatoes was large enough to offer for sale.

The sale of the Burbank potato helped out a little, but did not at first bring a large return. Notwithstanding the very obvious merits of this potato, time was required to educate people to appreciate it. They were accustomed to a red potato, and a white one, even though larger, smoother, and more productive, and of better quality, did not seem at first a tangible substitute. But in the course of time the Burbank potato made its way, as has elsewhere been related, until it became the leading potato of the Pacific Coast. Long before this, however, I had ceased to grow the potato. It was only during the first few years, before its cultivation became general, that I could profitably grow it for seed purposes.

I began my nursery business at Santa Rosa by raising such fruits and vegetables as gave promise of being immediately acceptable to the people of the vicinity. At that time the possibilities of California as a fruit center were for the most part vaguely realized, and it was first necessary to educate the Californians themselves to a recognition of the fact that in the soil and climate of their State were the potentialities of greater wealth than had ever been stored in the now almost depleted gold mines.

Once that lesson had been learned, there would be no great difficulty about disposing of the fruit, for the railways either built or projected insured facilities for transportation.

MY FIRST ADVERTISEMENT

When I first came to California I brought with me a few specimens of the Burbank potato. These were multiplied for two or three seasons, and then offered for sale "for trial on this coast." The success of the "trial" is evident in the fact that whole regions of California and Oregon are now given over to the exclusive growing of the Burbank potato, millions and millions of bushels each season.

00 Acres.

[Tree.]
at Depot

ay Station.

NTS.

 k of pure

ants.

dive, said to
Miners' Great
productive.
TRIAL PRESS
inches in cir-
at American,
ack," "Kerr's
Cum-
oyden," "Pres-

tion, and fiffewers the best stock of
We also offer a large stock of JAPANESE PERSIM-
MONS, transplanted. Monterey Cypress, for hedges, Blue
Gum and Pines for forest planting, Japan Mandarin, Orange,
Camellias and Camphor Trees at low figures. Address for
Catalogue and Price List.

WM. SEXTON,
Petaluma, Sonoma County, Cal.

Burbank's Seedling. To

This already famous Potato is now for the first time
offered by the originator for trial on this Coast. For description see *American Agriculturist*, for March, 1878.
PRICES: 1 lb. by mail, 50 cts.; 3 lbs. by mail, $1.00; 25
lbs. by express, $5.00.

LUTHER BURBANK, Nurseryman.
Santa Rosa, Sonoma County, Cal.

LOS GATOS NURSERIES.
SAN JOSE, CAL.

S. NEWHALL - - - Proprietor.

A large and general assortment of FRUIT and ORNA-
MENTAL TREES, Evergreens, Flowering Shrubs, Roses,
Greenhouse Plants, Grapevines, Small Fruits, etc. I offer
for sale a large and well assorted stock, Low-topped,
stalky Fruit Trees a specialty. Address

square t
Cor

The u

HAW

That ma
KET RA
sumer

Withe
He also
Buyers to
commiss

Nos

rano

As to the latter point, however, the conditions were very different from what they now are. The refrigerator car had not come into use, and the possibility of transporting fresh fruits across the continent at a reasonable cost seemed remote. So it was natural that such fruits as the prune and the olive were the ones that chiefly attracted attention. Their products could be transported anywhere, and there was an established market that was practically inexhaustible.

But, as already intimated, the region about Santa Rosa at the time of my coming was preeminently a wheat country, and the farmers in general were far more interested in cereals than in fruit of any kind. It was only after the wheat crops began to fail, through exhaustion of the soil for the special nutrients that this cereal demands, that the thoughts of the farming population in general could be directed toward fruit culture.

It is necessary to make this explanation because nowadays everyone thinks of California as preeminently a fruit country; and so it would not be obvious, without this elucidation, why one could not start in the nursery business at Santa Rosa in the year 1876, and hope for immediate patronage and a reasonable return for his labors.

But even if the market had been more certain, it would doubtless have been difficult for me to get a start, because fruit trees cannot be brought to a condition of bearing, or even to a stage where cions for grafting are available, in a short time. And I had neither capital nor credit, being virtually a stranger in a strange land.

So it was necessary to continue to gain a livelihood by working at carpentry, in which vocation I had now established a sufficient reputation to insure me pretty steady work. But every cent that I could earn, beyond the barest cost of maintenance, was put into stock for my prospective nursery; and, as has been said, the evening hours after the day's work with the plane, saw, and hammer was over, were devoted to the culture of seedlings.

The tedious and almost disheartening character of the task of establishing myself as a practical nurseryman at Santa Rosa may perhaps be illustrated about as tangibly as otherwise could be done by the citation of memoranda from old account books, which show that the total sales of nursery products in 1877, the first year that my nursery was supposed to be in operation, amounted to just $15.20. The products that brought this munificent return are listed as "Nursery stock and ornamental and flowering plants."

The following year, 1878, the total return from the nursery sales was $84.

The third year the sales amounted to $353.28. The fourth year they came to $702. And it was not until 1881, when the nursery had been for five years in operation, that the aggregate returns from the sale of its products of all descriptions passed the thousand dollar mark. The specific figure, in 1881, was $1,112.69.

The figures thus baldly presented tell their own story. They show that the nursery business in California forty-five years ago was in far different condition from what it is to-day.

Within ten years the quality of the trees and the reliability of the stock in general of the Burbank Nursery had become so widely known that I was selling more than $16,000 worth of stock per year. In the light of this ultimate prosperity, the privations of the earlier years may very well be minimized, even though they cannot quite be forgotten.

There are many incidents of that early period of probation, when struggling to establish myself as a nurseryman, in order that ultimately I might take up my plans for plant development on a large scale, that would have a measure of interest and would not be without importance in their bearing on the later work; but I must content my-

self with the narration of a single incident, partly
because it has to do with an event that was at the
time of momentous importance to me, inasmuch
as it gave a much-needed monetary return, and
at the same time served to advertise the work;
and partly because it illustrates in detail the possibility of rapidly laying the foundations for an
orchard, and hence may be of value to some other
plant experimenters.

Twenty Thousand Prune Trees

The incident in question has to do with the
production of twenty thousand prune trees, well
rooted and ready to transplant for permanent
location in an orchard, in a single season.

It was in the fourth year of my attempt at the
development of a nursery business at Santa Rosa
—that is to say, in the season of 1881—that I
produced the twenty thousand prune trees in
response to a "rush order," and in so doing forti-
fied a reputation for reliability and resourcefulness that my earlier work had begun to
establish.

The order for twenty thousand prunes was
given by Mr. Warren Dutton, a wealthy merchant and banker of Tomales, and later of San
Francisco, who had conceived a sudden interest
in prune growing and wished to undertake it on

a large scale with the least possible delay. Mr. Dutton had seen something of my work, and he came to me in March, 1881, and asked if I could furnish him twenty thousand prune trees ready to set out the coming fall.

At first thought I was disposed to answer that no one on earth could furnish twenty thousand fruit trees on an order given in March for delivery in the fall of the same year. But, after thinking the matter over for a few minutes, I decided that the project was not quite so hopeless as it seemed.

If almond seedlings were used for stock, and prune buds June-budded on these stocks, the thing might be accomplished.

Mr. Dutton agreed to furnish what financial aid was needed during the summer to pay for help and to purchase the required number of almonds for planting. So the bargain was closed, and I entered on the task with enthusiasm. What made the project seem feasible was the knowledge of the fact that almonds, under proper conditions, sprout almost at once like corn, unlike nearly all other stone fruits. I estimated that could the almonds be secured at once, and bedded in coarse sand for sprouting, they would furnish seedlings that could be planted in nursery rows in time for June budding.

VIEW IN THE SANTA ROSA GARDENS

This picture gives a very good idea of the way in which every inch of ground is utilized in our gardens at Santa Rosa. Note, however, that the beds are sharply delimited by board borders, and that there is evidence of orderly arrangement — profusion of plants of many species, but quite without confusion.

There was no difficulty about securing the almonds for planting, so the enterprise was almost instantly under way. In addition to the two acres of land which were then available in my nursery, I rented five additional acres; and a large number of men were engaged to plant the almonds in nursery rows as soon as they began to sprout.

The almonds were spread on a well-drained bed of creek sand and covered with coarse burlap cloth, which in turn was covered with a layer of sand about an inch in depth. In this way we could examine the almonds without any trouble, by lifting one end of the cloth.

The seeds commenced to sprout in less than fourteen days. Those which sprouted were carefully removed and planted in the nursery rows; the others were covered again, and each day more and more would be found sprouting.

The almonds were planted about four inches apart in the rows, the rows about four feet apart, on a piece of land adjoining the creek—a plot now covered with fine residences, and known as "Ludwig's Addition."

They began showing growth above ground in a short time, and the ground was very carefully cultivated.

By the time the buds in a neighbor's prune orchard were ready for use, the young almond trees were also ready. Toward the last of June, and in July and August, a large force of budders were employed in placing the French prune buds on the almond stalks.

After about ten days, when the buds had thoroughly united with the stalk, the tops of the young trees were broken over about eight inches from the ground; great care being exercised not to break them entirely off, but only to break the top down and still keep it alive.

If the top is broken or cut entirely off, the young trees are about certain to die. This is a mistake which many nurserymen make in trying to grow June buds, but by bending the tops over and leaving them on, none of the trees die, and the buds start much better than by any other plan.

Soon the young prune buds began to burst forth. These were carefully tied up alongside the stalk, and when they were a foot or more in height the old almond top was wholly cut away.

By December first, about 19,500 of the trees were ready for the planter; the others were furnished the next season.

Mr. Dutton was greatly pleased, as he had been told by all other nurserymen that it was absolutely impossible to produce trees in eight months, and he was very anxious to get a prune orchard at once. By systematic and energetic work we were able to meet his exceptional needs. Never before or since, I believe, was a 200-acre orchard developed in a single season.

SUCCESS AT LAST

As suggested, the feat of producing the twenty thousand prunes served to advertise this work locally. Meantime the reputation for dependableness of the Santa Rose nursery products had been greatly extending, in a very modest way to be sure, yet with cumulative effect.

Also the general knowledge that prunes constituted a profitable crop was spreading, and about this time the demand for prune trees became very great. Naturally my reputation as a producer of prune stock was enhanced by the demonstration given with the twenty thousand young trees. Prunes that had been grown in smaller lots gave equal satisfaction to purchasers in various regions. Great pains had been taken that no tree should leave the nursery that was not exactly true to name, and in all respects precisely as represented. And now I began to reap the benefits.

The quest of prune trees became such a hobby that it came to be the current jest when anyone was asked for to respond: "Well, if you do not find him in town, you will probably find him at Burbank's waiting for some trees."

In course of time more land was needed, the four-acre place in the very heart of Santa Rosa was purchased which was in future to be my home and the seat of many of the most important experiments.

This place was then a neglected, run-down plot which had been on the market for many years. The land was about as poor as could be found anywhere. Many attempts had been made to cultivate it, but a crop had not been grown upon it for a long time, if ever.

Such a plot of land did not seem to offer great inducements for a nurseryman. But I had a plan in mind that would transform it.

The first move was to place tiles under the whole tract at a depth of four feet, thus draining the land which had at one time been the bottom of a pond. At the same time the ground was carefully graded. Then, as stable manure could be had for the hauling 1,800 loads of it were obtained, and delivered on the four acres. This was spread so thickly that it was impossible to plow it under without the aid of several men, who followed the plow and pitched the fertilizer into furrows as the plowing proceeded.

Further details as to the method of tillage and the preparation of the soil have been given in an earlier chapter and need not be repeated here. But the subject is mentioned because I wish to emphasize the possibility of transforming very poor land into land of exceptional fertility.

To what extent intelligent manipulation of land may be rewarded is illustrated in the immediate sequel. For in the spring following the season in which the new land was tiled and fertilized, it was planted to fruit tree seedlings, and the year following enough nursery stock was sold from half the land to pay for the entire place and all the improvements that had been made.

So I now had a four-acre plot of the finest land, located near the business center of Santa Rosa, that had been paid for with ingenuity and knowledge without making any serious drain on the purse.

This same plot of land, modified in places by treating with sand to make it suitable for raising bulbs, has perhaps grown a greater number of varieties of plants from regions near and remote than were ever elsewhere grown on any four acres of the earth's surface.

The Long-Deferred Project

By about the year 1884 I was thoroughly established with a nursery business that gave me a sure income of ten thousand dollars or more per year, and nothing more was required than to continue along the lines of this established work to insure a life of relative ease and financial prosperity.

But nothing was farther from my thoughts than the permanent following of the routine business of the nurseryman. At no stage of the work in California had I given up the expectation of devoting the best years of my life to plant experimentation and the development of new races of useful fruits and vegetables, and of beautiful flowers. And now the time seemed to have arrived when the long-deferred project could be put into execution.

So from the very hour when the nursery business had come to be fully established, plans were made for giving it up.

The practical work in the nursery itself had, of course, furnished a most valuable schooling. I had learned the technique of growing seedlings, and grafting, and the general routine of practical plant culture. And this obviously was knowledge of a kind that would be of inestimable importance when I came to deal with rare exotics and with new forms of plant life. The practical knowledge of how best to nurse a tender seedling has had its full share in the furtherance of the successes of later years.

Meantime a comprehensive knowledge of the native plants of California had been gained through having collected their seeds and bulbs for eastern and foreign seedsmen.

At about this time there was an interest in the native plants of California, and many nurserymen were anxious to give them a trial. During those years when my own nursery business was only formative by gathering seeds and bulbs on orders from various eastern and foreign firms my income was increased. In the course of this work various trips were made to the surrounding territory. On two occasions, in 1880 and in 1881, I visited the region of the geysers, which was found to be a productive locality for new material. And everywhere careful study was made of the vegetation, both with an eye to the immediate collection of seeds and bulbs, and for future reference in connection with the projected work.

The knowledge thus gained served well in later years in suggesting material for hybridizing experiments.

MIDSUMMER'S VIEW

This is a view across the center of the main garden at Santa Rosa, with our new home (which is really situated across the street) at the left. The tree with heavily massed foliage towering above the building at the right is the hybrid elm.

Moreover, the work of collecting, preserving, and shipping seeds, plants, and bulbs taught practical lessons that were of great importance later in the instruction of my own collectors in foreign lands, who gathered the materials that have had so large a share in the production of new plant forms that finally appeared in my experiment gardens.

It would have pleased me greatly to extend the botanizing explorations to still wider territories, and after the nursery business had come to be fully established, about the year 1884, it would have been quite feasible to do so.

The work was so organized that it might readily have been left to assistants for periods of a year or more, during which I could have traveled and observed the plant products that seemed to invite importation.

But to have done this would have been to break in on the plan of the projected life work that had already been to some extent interrupted for a period of about eight years, during which I had found it impossible to carry out new experiments, except on a limited scale. Longer delay was not to be thought of, being eager to take up the projected work, and it was not deferred for a season longer than was absolutely necessary.

Even before I could see my way to the abandonment of the practical work of the nurseryman, projects were in hand that were preparing
the way for the new activities. In particular, I
had sent to Japan to secure seeds and cuttings of
a great variety of fruits. It seemed certain that I
could better afford to hire collectors in foreign
lands to secure material than to go to foreign
lands in person in quest of it.

The first consignment of Japanese seeds and
seedlings arrived November 5, 1884. And when
the consignment was in hand, with the representatives of exotic species of fruits, I felt that a
new era had begun for me, and that the long-
frustrated plans were about to find realization.

The following year, so well had the nursery
business prospered, I was able to purchase a farm
at Sebastopol, seven miles from Santa Rosa,
where the conditions were more favorable for the
growing of certain types of plants.

The second consignment from Japan, including the plum, whose story has elsewhere been told
in detail, came December 20, 1885. The place at
Sebastopol where they were to be planted and
nurtured was purchased eight days later. And
with this purchase the project of devoting a lifetime to the work of plant experimentation was
fairly and finally inaugurated. For the Sebas-

topol place, with its eighteen acres, was not purchased for use as a practical nursery, but solely as an experiment garden.

With the development of the Sebastopol place, a new phase of life work began.

Thenceforward my time was divided between the experiment gardens at Santa Rosa and that at Sebastopol, and upon one place or the other nearly all my experiments in plant development were to be performed.

An interest in the nursery business was retained for two or three years more, to furnish money to carry out the initial stages of the new experiments; for of course it could not be expected that new varieties of fruits and flowers would spring into existence in a single season. Nor could immediate purchasers be found for them if they had been thus magically produced. But from the time when the place at Sebastopol was purchased it was determined that my energies were to be wholly devoted to the work of plant development—the work that had been projected, and at which a beginning had been made in New England, and the hope of continuing which had been the incentive to persistent efforts during the intervening years.

PATIENCE AND ITS REWARD

The Period of Achievement

THE purchase of the farm at Sebastopol
was made, as recorded in the preceding
chapter, on the 28th of December, 1885.
As this was to be the important chief testing
ground for trees and flowers, it may perhaps be
of interest to describe somewhat in detail the
farm itself and its topographical surroundings.
In particular an idea should be given of the
indigenous flora of the region, because many of
the wild species were utilized in experiments of
great interest and sometimes of importance.

The picture thus presented of the environment of the work will serve, perhaps, to give a
clearer understanding of some of its details.

The plot of land at Sebastopol is known as
the Gold Ridge farm, although the place has
usually been referred to in the preceding pages
merely as the experiment farm at Sebastopol.

The farm has a gradual and gentle slope toward the Santa Rosa valley. It is undulating

in contour, and its chief slopes face the east.
The soil is sandy, no doubt part of one of many
great sand dunes piled up by the waves of the
Pacific Ocean and the winds in past ages.

On this place there is a variety of soils and of
degrees of moisture. Some parts of the land are
so moist that the water seeps up to the surface
throughout the season, and the remainder is so
loose and friable that moisture may be found all
through the summer even six months after any
rain has fallen upon it.

NATIVE PLANTS

At the time the place was purchased about
two-thirds of it was covered with white and tan
oaks, the native Douglas spruce, manzanita, cascara sagrada, hazel, and madrona, while beneath
the trees grew honeysuckles, brodiæas, calochor-
tus, cynoglossum, wild peas, fritillarias, orchids,
sisyrinchiums—yellow and blue—and numerous
other wild plants and shrubs.

During the first few years following the clear-
ing away of this forest many species of clover
wholly new to me made their appearance,
twenty species or more. There was also an
abundance of alfilaria—*Erodium moschatum*—
a Chilean plant, belonging to the geranium
family. This and the clovers growing in the

water made a splendid crop to turn under in the spring, thus adding to the soil much nitrogen—among the most expensive of all fertilizing materials.

Later, three acres were added on one side of this place, and again three acres on another—of very similar soil—making now sixteen acres closely covered with numerous species of plants and trees used in the various experiments.

This farm is one of the most sightly places in the vicinity. In the middle foreground lies the broad Santa Rosa Valley with the city of Santa Rosa in the distance; and almost under one's feet is Sebastopol. Mount Saint Helena looms up grandly in the east some thirty miles away, more than four thousand feet in altitude. Most of the hills and mountains of the region are wooded with Douglas spruce, various oaks, madronas, and manzanitas. Along the streams, through the valley, grow Oregon maples, alders, ash, willows, and hawthorns.

Looking over the valley of Santa Rosa one sees one of the most prosperous communities anywhere to be found. In the early spring, great apple and prune orchards lighten the valley with a sheet of bloom; and, later, fields of hops here and there, with the vineyards along the foothills, make a most enchanting view. The

A SIMPLE BUT IMPORTANT EQUIPMENT

These simple garden tools are perhaps more often used than any others. The trowel is the universal transplanting implement. The other tools are soil looseners and weed exterminators. A small garden plot could be kept in order with these tools alone.

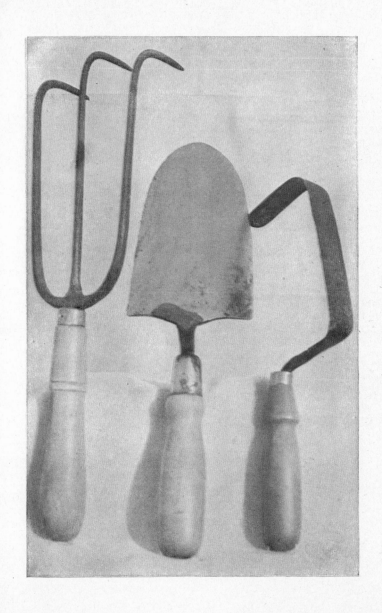

floor of the valley is like one great park dotted here and there with giant oaks, each one of a different form; here, perhaps, a hundred in a cluster, there a half dozen, artistically grouped as if by a landscape gardener. These are mostly western white oak (*Quercus lobata*) though in some parts of the valley there are numerous patches of the black oak (*Q. californica*) and along the streams the live oak (*Q. Wislizenii*).

In the distant hills north and east are a great variety of evergreen and deciduous trees and shrubs among the most common of which are the following conifers: the digger pine, sugar pine, the yellow pine, the knob-cone pine, coast redwood, incense cedar, MacNab cypress, Goven's cypress, and nutmeg tree.

Some of the other evergreen and deciduous trees growing in this immediate vicinity are: Oregon maple, box elder, Oregon ash, California buckeye, white alder, red alder, tanbark oak, white oak, Pacific post oak, black oak, blue oak, maul oak, mountain live oak, tree elder, bush elder, cottonwood, bayberry, madrona, golden chestnut, coast manzanita, and common manzanita.

There are ornamental shrubs in profusion; among others, the rhododendron, azalea, Juneberry, Judas tree, hawthorns, western sweet-scented shrub, California lilac, coast lilac, mahala mats (trailing or creeping lilac), buckthorn cascara, flowering dogwood, common dogwood, chokecherry, meadowsweet, wild apple, burning bush, poison oak, hazel, black willow, creek willow, velvet willow, snowberry, oso berry, chamissal, and salal.

Of vines and bearers of small fruit or of handsome flowers there are the wild grape, Oregon grape, mahonia, huckleberry, bilberry, low gooseberry, straggly gooseberry, cañon gooseberry, flowering currant, compact flowering currant, tree poppy, modest shrub, Labrador tea, redwood rose, California rose, Sonoma rose, silktassel tree, bear brush, yerba santa, yerba buena, perennial monkey flower, mistletoe, Dutchman's pipe, salmonberry, raspberry, thimbleberry, and almost innumerable smaller plants.

These glimpses of the indigenous flora of the immediate vicinity of the new experiment farm will serve to give an idea of the abundance of interesting native material, for the most part hitherto quite untouched by the plant experimenter, that awaited investigation.

ANTICIPATIONS

Had I felt at liberty to follow my own inclinations, paying no heed to the question of practical monetary returns, I could have found abundant material for the investigation of a lifetime without going outside the bounds of the Gold Ridge farm itself.

My own tastes would have led me to devote the major part of the time to the investigation of flowering plants and the development of flowers having hitherto unrevealed potentialities of form and color and odor. But it was obvious that one could not hope to make a living in this way. I knew that in order to have even a fair prospect of securing a monetary return that would enable me to keep up this work, once the nursery was abandoned, it would be necessary to produce marketable fruits.

In this field alone could one hope to find a ready sale for new plant developments, however striking or interesting from a scientific standpoint the results of experiments in other lines might prove.

And of course the indigenous wildlings of the immediate environment offered only scant material for the immediate production of new fruits of practical value. As a matter of course one must depend for material largely on the orchard fruits already under cultivation. These had been educated for countless generations. Most horticulturists regarded them as perfected beyond any hope of conspicuous further development. But in my own view what had been done with these fruits might better be regarded as a proof of their capacity for still further education and development.

In particular, I hoped, with the new material then being gathered from foreign countries to be able to undertake experiments in hybridizing and selection that might reasonably be expected to produce altogether novel results.

How fully this expectation has been justified, the reader is already partly aware. But it should be recalled that the things which now seem axiomatic because they have been accomplished had quite a different aspect from the standpoint of the year 1885. Hybridizations that have now been shown to be ready of accomplishment were then regarded as quite impossible by all horticulturists who gave the matter a thought.

As has been pointed out, the attitude among botanists and horticulturists generally was one of profound skepticism as to the possibility of developing modified races by hybridizations, or, indeed, by any means whatever within limited periods of time.

My own faith in the possibility of developing new races through crossing and selection had never faltered, however, since the earlier studies had given a clear view of the range of variation of plants both under natural conditions and under cultivation. And it may be taken as adequate proof of confidence that I purchased experiment farms and sent far and wide for hybridizing material at the very earliest moment when my financial conditions made such action possible.

Nor should it be understood that I had by any means entirely neglected experimental tests during all the period of my nursery experience. On the contrary, I had at all stages of this experience devoted as much time as could be spared to tests in cross-fertilizing and in selection among the various nursery products. These had served to give an expert knowledge of the results that might be expected from plant improvement. Tentative results had been attained that gave support to the most sanguine expectations.

Orchard and Garden Materials

Indeed, it was largely as the result of these experiments in selection that my nursery orchards had come to be of such quality as to command the attention of an ever-widening circle of fruit growers.

A very wide range of fruit-bearing, ornamental, and flowering plants were grown, and

SOIL-STIRRING IMPLEMENTS

Here are a few of the various types of plows and harrows, some of them to be drawn by horses, others pushed by hand. They are indispensable adjuncts of gardening on a comprehensive scale, though the tractors have now taken the place of horses.

although no new plants had been produced that could be compared with those of a later period, the nursery had been stocked with the very best existing varieties of different groups of fruits and flowers, and all had been submitted to careful comparative tests until those that remained were of exceptional quality, and thousands of new productions were under way that were undeveloped.

The nursery catalogue issued in 1887—the year before the nursery was sold preparatory to devoting my entire time to the experiment gardens then in an advanced stage of preparation—comprises 24 pages, and preserves the list of the exceptional varieties of horticultural plants that had been selected and developed and supplied the material for continuance and extension of the experiments on a larger scale on the test ground at Sebastopol.

Here were orchard fruits in great variety; small fruits of the choicest types; nuts of several species, including chestnut, walnut, and pecan; garden vegetables, including asparagus and rhubarb; a long list of deciduous ornamental trees and shrubs, and an even longer list of evergreens; vines and trailing shrubs in interesting variety; and elaborate series of roses, hedge plants, bulbous plants, and bedding plants in general. All these had been collected and selected and prepared for this very purpose.

With such materials at hand, it was obviously possible to continue the work of developing new varieties on an expansive scale so soon as the grounds were ready, and as we have already seen, shipments of plants from Japan began to be received even before the Sebastopol farm was purchased.

MATERIALS FROM ABROAD

The year following the purchase of the farm, grafts of twelve varieties of New Zealand apples were imported. And from this time forward I was constantly in receipt of shipments of seeds or bulbs or cions of rare or interesting plants from all regions of the world.

Association was established with foreign collectors who made a business of securing plants. And as the work became known in the course of succeeding years, amateur collectors everywhere were kind enough to send me materials, so that the experiment gardens became a testing ground for seeds of many thousands of species that had never before been grown in America.

Much of this is already known to the reader of the early chapters of this work, but the facts are emphasized anew because an understanding of them is essential to the comprehension of the work that was being carried forward.

The very essence of the new method was to bring together, through hybridization, plant strains that had been long separated, making possible the recombination of hereditary factors in such a way as to bring out, combine, and intensify racial traits.

Obviously such an attempt requires the cooperation of collectors living in widely separated regions. Explorers, missionaries, teachers, travelers, botanists, sailors, and others by thousands have placed at my disposal seeds, bulbs, and plants from the whole world with never a thought of personal reward. The native Indians of many parts of North America, but more especially South America, have been pressed into this service, as they of all others know where the best wild plants and flowers are to be found and thus have the opportunity to gather their seeds. Through the teachings of explorers, missionaries, and travelers, they have, in many cases, been trained to become unusually good collectors.

I wish here to pay especial tribute to the faithful service that has been rendered both by professional collectors and by amateurs who knew me by reputation only and who had no thought of reward beyond the satisfaction of aiding in a work calculated to benefit humanity at large.

Through these collectors I have frequently obtained wild plants the economic value of which had never been suspected, and which might otherwise have remained unknown, which, when combined with plants already in hand, proved of inestimable value in the development of new varieties of great scientific interest or of practical importance.

Methods and Objects Sought

To give details as to the methods by which I sought to blend the qualities of the plants that furnished materials for the new investigations when the experiment gardens were fairly in operation, would be to repeat what has been told in earlier volumes of this work.

The record of the results of these experiments makes up the main bulk of all these volumes. So it obviously is not desirable that I should attempt to repeat here, even in epitome, what has else-where been told in detail. Yet a few general comments on methods and results may be of interest.

Also it may not be amiss, by way of summary, to outline very briefly the chronological sequence of the chief lines of endeavor of the period, now approaching the termination of its half century, during which the development of improved races of plants has been comprehensively carried forward.

In the successive chapters that have told of the different lines of endeavor, plants were naturally grouped according to their botanical relations or their economic uses, with only incidental reference to the date of the experiment through which this or that particular variety was developed.

Perhaps, then, it will serve to coordinate the work as a whole if we review in partial outline the story of the endeavors of successive periods; bearing in mind, of course, that many hundreds of experiments were always being carried forward simultaneously, and that many experiments that achieved notable results at an early day, are still being carried forward to obtain results even more notable.

Taking the widest and most general view, it may be said that the chief lines of investigation at the outset of the period when my energies were turned exclusively to experimental work, instead of being hampered by ordinary nursery duties, had to do with the improvement of orchard fruits on one hand and with certain flowering plants on the other. From the outset,

SEEDS IN THE GREENHOUSE

A corner of the greenhouse in seed gathering time. Seeds of many varieties are here collected for drying, preparatory to being stored for the winter or immediately planted, as the case may be. Note the sieves at hand, to be used if necessary in screening out impurities, or separating seeds of different sizes.

however, small fruits were given almost equal attention.

It had been made clear to me, through nursery experience, that the varieties of fruits grown in California at that time, being all of eastern and European origin, were not ideally adapted to the new climatic conditions of the Pacific Coast. It seemed desirable that new varieties adapted to the new conditions should be produced.

So one prime object of the early work was to develop orchard fruits, and notably prunes, plums, peaches, apples, and pears, that would be of value in the development of the fruit indus-try in California, but I had in mind also the desir-ability of producing fruits that would be adapted to growth in other parts of the world. Most of the fruits then existing were lacking in impor-tant qualities that are equally essential wherever the fruit is grown.

It was determined from the outset to give par-ticular attention to these matters, endeavoring to produce varieties of fruit trees that would be hardy and resistant to unfavorable conditions and that would be not only heavy but regular bearers. The matter of resistance to insect pests and to disease was also given very careful con-sideration from the outset.

Seedlings that showed susceptibility were ruthlessly weeded out, and the survivors became the parents of races that are relatively immune to disease.

Of course the combination of different species to bring together long-diverged racial strains was a fundamental part of the plan. Unnumbered thousands of hand-pollenizing experiments were made each year, and the limits of affinity between the different species were tested by ceaseless and persistent efforts.

When species that were apparently somewhat closely related proved infertile after cross-pollination, it was not taken for granted that there was real antagonism between those species until the experiment had been tried over and over in successive seasons, perhaps hundreds of times in the case of a single pair of species, often using different individuals and varieties of species.

Instances in which a hybridizing experiment at last proved successful after many years of failure—as for example in the case of the sunberry—will be recalled by the reader.

PRACTICAL AND SCIENTIFIC INTERESTS COMBINED

In general, practical results were sought rather than the establishment of theories; yet for the most part, in such a line of experiment theory and practice necessarily go together.

The only sharp distinction between our method and that of an experimenter who is looking only to the investigation of the laws of heredity is that we were obliged to select for preservation a few only among large companies of hybrid seedlings, destroying the rest, and to that extent making the record incomplete. It would be of great scientific interest to trace the entire company of a hybrid stock as to all its individual members through successive generations.

But when the members of a fraternity number ten or a hundred thousand or a million, as was often the case in our experiments, the attempt to preserve all and to investigate their progeny through several generations would necessitate the expansion of our experiment farm until it comprised thousands of acres, and the employment of an army of helpers.

If this is true of the plants of a single series of experiments, what shall we say of the aggregate companies making up the ranks of plants involved in two or three thousand experiments. So soon as our work was well under way, and throughout all the succeeding years, at least three thousand different series of experiments have been carried forward simultaneously.

Very commonly a million seedlings are involved in a single fraternity.

Under these conditions, it will be obvious that there was no choice but to select the few individuals that came nearest to the ideals of a mental forecast, ruthlessly destroying the rest to make room for the favored ones.

And in so doing we were of course duplicating the method of nature herself, although the qualities that determined our choice in any given case were not usually those that would have fitted the chosen individuals for preservation in a natural environment. Our selections were made, of course, with the object of fitting the plant to meet human needs and tastes. The selections of nature are made with reference to the needs of the plant itself.

But if we make allowance for this difference in the point of view, we may say that the principle of selection is exactly the same in each case.

And we are justified, no doubt, in saying that the experiments in artificial selection made on my experiment farms during the period under review, constitute the most elaborate series of experimental proofs of the truth of the Darwinian theory of Natural Selection that have ever been brought forward.

Such experiments in hybridizing and selection as were part of the everyday work at Santa Rosa and Sebastopol, season after season, involving thousands of species, had been performed elsewhere only in isolated cases and by rare exception. Nowhere else had such a work been undertaken on a comprehensive scale even with a few species of plants.

The application of the method to thousands of species, involving countless myriads of individuals, was an absolute novelty.

SCIENTIFIC RESULTS

The results of the work in their bearings on scientific theory may be briefly summarized.

These experiments demonstrated that the barriers between natural species are much more fragile than had been almost universally supposed.

They showed that not only may we produce fertile hybrids between a very large number of related species of plants, but that equally fertile hybrids may often be produced by the union of species that are so widely separated as to be classified in different genera.

They have proved that the first-generation hybrids may resemble one parent or the other pretty closely or may show a blending of quali-

CLEANING SEEDS

That "trifles make perfection" is as true of gardening as of any other art. One of the trifles that is often neglected by the amateur is the careful cleaning of seeds, if necessary by washing, to minimize danger of injury from fungous growths or insects, and to guard against the inclusion of foreign seeds or impurities of any kind. An electric power seed separator is used for larger lots.

ties; and that in the second generation, with rare exceptions, there is a segregation and recombination of the racial qualities of the original parent species, in which the extreme forms may more or less closely duplicate one parent or the other, and the intermediate forms may show almost every conceivable gradation between the two.

They have demonstrated, further, that it is possible, by selecting among the second-generation hybrids the individuals that exhibit any desired combination of qualities, to develop, in the course of a few generations of inbreeding, races in which this combination of qualities is so accentuated and fixed as to constitute a distinguishing characteristic of a new variety quite unlike the original forms.

Moreover, that the later-generation hybrids might reveal racial traits that were not observable in either of the parent species.

The segregation and redistribution of characters often gave opportunity for the appearance of qualities that have long been submerged, which by cumulative selection produced new characters and qualities never before in existence.

As a tangible illustration, hybrids in the first generation may show an enhanced capacity for growth, and the later generation hybrids may be graded from groups of dwarfs at one end of the

scale to giants at the other. A corresponding
gradation may be shown in regard to other qualities, such as color of flower, character of leaf,
flavor of fruit, productivity, resistance to disease
—in a word as to all the varied properties that
go to make up the personality—if the expression
be permitted—of a plant.

Many of these things are so well recognized
to-day that they seem mere matters of fact, quite
beyond challenge. But they were matters of
very ardent challenge in the day when they were
first being demonstrated in the experiment
gardens at Santa Rosa and Sebastopol.

When the first official announcements of this
work were sent forth, through publication of the
brochure called "New Creations in Fruits and
Flowers" in June, 1893, the measure of the
novelty of the announcements may be gauged
by the popular interest aroused on one hand and
by the outspoken incredulity of the botanical and
horticultural worlds in general, save only the individual experts who had previously visited my
grounds and seen for themselves the truth of the
matters that were now given publicity.

It will serve to give an outline of the progress of the work if we briefly summarize the contents of the successive catalogues in which the
new developments were publicly reported.

New Developments Announced in 1893

The first of these, as already noted, appeared in June, 1893, under title of "New Creations in Fruits and Flowers." The subsequent ones were regarded as supplements to the original publication. By running over the contents of these supplements of successive years, an impression is gained of the sequence in which the more important plant developments were brought to a stage of improvement that justified their introduction. But of course it must not be inferred that the different experiments had been taken up in the precise sequence in which their successful results were announced. Some lines of investigation require far more time than others; there are a great number of experiments still awaiting announcement that were begun at the very outset of my experimental work.

Nevertheless the successive announcements may be taken as at least giving a general view of the progress of the work; so we may briefly summarize the contents of the original publication and of the earlier supplements to which chief interest attaches because of the entire novelty of the products they present.

In a later chapter we shall take up the theoretical bearings of the new work. Here we are

concerned for the most part with a bald recital
of the names of the more important new varieties of plant life, presented somewhat in the
order of their introduction. Even as to these,
nothing like a complete list will be given, for the
minor improvements of plant life, large numbers of which have been referred to in the course
of this work, do not call for special reference here.

Even the recital of the names that cannot well
be overlooked may carry us to rather tiresome
lengths.

The new varieties of hybrid plants announced
in the publication of 1893 are listed in eighteen
successive groups, as follows:

(1) Hybrid Walnuts, including the forms
named the Paradox and the Royal. The pedigrees of the two hybrids are given, one
being a cross between the California and the
Persian walnut and the other between the
black walnut of the East and the California
black walnut; but the distinctive names were
given later.

(2) A new Japanese Mammoth Chestnut.
The origin of this chestnut is given, and it is
stated that the one offered is "the best one of
more than ten thousand seedlings, a tree which
every season bears all it can hold of fat, glossy

nuts of the very largest size and as sweet as the American chestnut."

(3) Two Quinces, named respectively the Van Deman and Santa Rosa, the former named in honor of the Chief of the Pomological Department of the United States Department of Agriculture, who had particularly admired it. A new Japan quince named Alpha, and a new flowering quince named Dazzle.

(4) Plums and Prunes. These comprised ten new varieties or hybrids, for the most part bearing numbers only, but including the Golden, the Delaware, the Shipper, and the plums that afterward were famous as the Wickson and America; also the Giant and Splendor prunes.

(5) Hybrid and crossbred Berries. Here there are nineteen new varieties, including the Japanese Golden Mayberry, the Primus berry, the berry named Humboldt, afterward changed by the purchaser to Phenomenal, and the Paradox, Autumn Giant, and Eureka. The strange raspberry-strawberry hybrids are also described and pictured, although not offered for sale.

(6) Seedling Roses and rose hybrids. There are five named or numbered varieties in this list, including the Peachblow and the one afterward known as Santa Rosa, and one named later Burbank by the purchaser. A number of Rugosa

A COLLECTION OF SIEVES

These sieves are, of course, merely fine screens conveniently framed, so that they can be used for various purposes — screening compost, cleaning seeds, etc.

hybrids are listed in addition, one of them being mentioned as having received a medal from the California State Floral Society.

(7) New Callas. These included the variegated Little Gem, the Snow Flake, the Giant Calla, and the Golden variegated *Richardia alba maculata,* it being recorded of the first named that it was selected from eighteen thousand seedlings, and of the last named that it was the single selection among hundreds of thousands of bulbs of the spotted-leaved Calla that had been raised for the trade from seed on my grounds.

(8) Hybrid Lilies. Only two specified varieties are offered under individual numbers, one being the large-flowering *Lilium pardalinum,* afterward known as Fragrance, and the other a dwarf form—growing only ten inches high and producing from twenty to forty blossoms on each of the short stalks—which afterward bore the name of Glow. But the names of forty-two species and varieties were given as only a partial list of the lilies that had been combined in the hybrid seedlings which even at that time made up an extraordinary colony in the experiment garden.

It was stated that some of the older hybrids and seedlings were represented by as many as a thousand bulbs each; that half a million kinds were yet to unfold their petals for the first time; and that we were still planting from one to three pounds of hybridized lily seed every season.

So the varieties actually announced were only the forerunners of a vast company of which more would be heard in later years.

(9) New varieties of Gladiolus. It was stated that six of the best forms of this flower, from among a million or more seedlings raised during the ten years preceding, had been intro- duced four years earlier, one of these being the first double gladiolus and the first of a type in which the flowers are closely arranged all around the spike, like a hyacinth. In the catalogue ten interesting forms were listed and succinctly described, among others a white form with very large flowers, several dwarfs with curious stripes and markings, and sundry double forms.

(10) Hybrid Clematis. Six new forms were named, including a double variety, with broad snow-white petals, the flowers five to six inches in diameter, that blooms almost constantly throughout spring, summer, and fall. Another variety was said to resemble a white water lily, and it was said of the group that "No hardy flower except the rose and the lily is so mag- nificently beautiful as the new hybrid Clematis;

seedlings of which have been grown at the rate of ten thousand a year for several years."

(11) A new Myrtle. This is described as a new silver variegated Roman Myrtle or Brides' Myrtle, originated as early as 1882. It had been characterized by the California State Gardener as the handsomest variegated shrub he had ever seen.

(12) A new Poppy named Silver Lining. Described as developed by six years' selection from a sport of the *Papaver umbrosum* (Butterfly Poppy), and as being of a glistening silver white on the inside of each petal instead of crimson and black; the outside remaining of the original brilliant crimson, thus producing a strikingly beautiful effect.

(13) A new plant, the Nicotunia. This name had been coined to describe a new race produced by crossing a tobacco plant (*Nicotiana*) with a Petunia. A suggestion of the difficulties involved in making this cross was given in these words:

"If anyone thinks he can take right hold and produce Nicotunias as he would hybrid petunias or crossbred primroses, let him try; there is no patent on their manufacture; but if the five hundredth crossing succeeds, or even the five thousandth, under the best conditions obtainable, he will surely be very successful; I do not fear any immediate competition."

It was stated that the flowers of the new hybrid are handsome, white, pink, carmine, or striped, and are borne in bounteous profusion, but that no seed is ever produced, although the plants are very readily multiplied by cuttings.

(14) Hybrid Nicotianas. These are hybrids produced by crossing six or more different species of *Nicotiana*. "Many of the new hybrid varieties are only obtained after several thousand crossings, under all conditions which seemed to promise success; but now I have perennial varieties with glaucous green foliage, edged and mottled with white, bearing pink blossoms in cymes two or three feet across with from five hundred to two thousand or more blossoms in each cyme. Most of these hybrids are readily propagated from root cuttings or slips; none of them ever bear any seed; all are unusually hardy."

(15) Begonia-Leafed Squash. "A mammoth squash which produced abundant crops for stock feeding and has bright golden variegated leaves. The unusual leaf variegation appeared four years ago (1889) on a single vine, and by selection has become so fixed that at least 95 per cent are variegated. The form, size, and uni-

form appearance of the squashes has also been very greatly improved."

(16) New Potatoes. Two varieties are described as being the best of several thousand seedlings that have been tested for five years. One is a long, nearly cylindrical, smooth, white seedling of the Burbank; the other is a short, flattish, oval, light-colored potato with a russet coat, from a cross of the old "Chile" or "Bodega Red" and the Burbank. "Both are superior keepers, and have never shown any tendency to become diseased."

(17) Ornamental Crossbred Tomato. This new fruiting plant is named Combination and is described as a cross between the "Little Currant" and the "Dwarf Champion" tomatoes. "The curious plaited, twisted, and blistered, but handsome leaves, sturdily compact growth, and clusters of fruit, will make it a favored ornamental plant which can be easily grown by everybody."

(18) "Other New Plants." A miscellaneous list of hybrids, including some very extraordinary combinations, particularly crosses between the different orchard fruits, peaches, almonds, plums, quinces, and apples in various combinations. The photograph of a stem of apetalous pistillate blossoms of a plum-apricot hybrid is

given; a picture that has peculiar interest now in view of the subsequent development of the plumcot. Mention is also made of the crossbred tigridias, new cannas, arums, amaryllis, brodiæas, aquilegias, and asters, and a multitude of other things not yet near enough to perfection to merit a special description. These were to appear in later catalogues.

A SUMMARY OF CONCLUSIONS

The list of "New Creations" thus briefly summarized occupies fifty pages.

There follows a concluding section under the heading "Facts and Possibilities" that summarizes the work and that may be worth quoting here for its historical interest. The general attitude of the experimenter toward his work in both its theoretical and its practical bearings is rather clearly outlined in the summary concluding a catalogue which so high an authority as Professor Hugo de Vries has seen fit to describe as of an epoch-making character:

"There is no possible room for doubt that every form of plant life existing on the earth is now being and has always been modified, more or less, by its surroundings, and often rapidly and permanently changed, never to return to the same form.

"When man takes advantage of these facts, and changes all the conditions, giving abundance of room for expansion and growth, extra cultivation and a superabundance of the various chemical elements in the most assimilable form, with abundance of light and heat, great changes sooner or later occur according to the susceptibility of the subject; and when, added to all these combined governing forces, we employ the other potent forces of combination and selection of the best combinations, the power to improve our useful and ornamental plants is limitless."

TEN YEARS OF PROGRESS

In describing this work, Professor de Vries has said that my catalogue of 1893, the contents of which have just been summarized, gained for its author "a world-wide reputation and brought him into connection with almost all of the larger horticultural firms on the earth."

These catalogues were largely bought up by the United States Experiment Stations and various American and European universities to be used as textbooks.

It would be superfluous to recapitulate in detail the plant developments that have occupied attention at Santa Rosa and Sebastopol in the more recent years.